# VOLUME 13

# FUNK & WAGNALLS WILDLIFE ENCYCLOPEDIA

GENERAL EDITORS • Dr. Maurice Burton and Robert Burton

*Also published as The International Wildlife Encyclopedia and Encyclopedia of Animal Life.*

Funk & Wagnalls, Inc., New York, New York

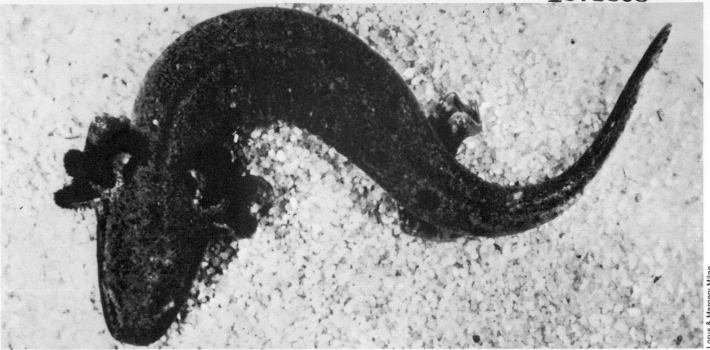

Lorus & Margery Milne

# Mudpuppy

*The mudpuppy is a kind of salamander living in the weedy streams, ponds and rivers of parts of North America. In the southern part of its range it is called water dog. Both names depend on a belief that it makes a barking sound.*

*It grows up to 2 ft long, although it is usually about 1 ft long, and is grey to rusty or dark brown with indistinct bluish-black spots and mottlings. There is a conspicuous dark mark on the side of the head running through the eye. Its short, weak legs are suitable only for crawling over mud and are held against the sides when swimming. Each foot has four fairly long toes. Just behind the head are three pairs of conspicuous, bushy and velvety red, plume-like gills. The head is flat and squarish with small eyes.*

*The mudpuppy ranges from southern Canada to the Gulf of Mexico, from the Mississippi and Missouri basins to New Jersey, and eight subspecies or forms are recognized. A dwarf mudpuppy lives in the Neuse River in North Carolina and the largest form lives in the rice field ditches of both North and South Carolina.*

### Asking to be caught

Mudpuppies, slow and sluggish salamanders, often take bait, getting themselves hooked, to the annoyance of fishermen. As well as losing his bait the fisherman finds the mudpuppy a slippery customer to handle, due to the slime-covered body. Inevitably this has led to the idea that the mudpuppy is poisonous, which is partly true. It has poison glands in its skin but the poison is not strong enough to affect human beings. Some people claim mudpuppies are good to eat, and one writer speaks of their fine quality and white flesh, rivalling frogs' legs in flavour, and yielding as much meat as a dozen frogs.

*The mudpuppy (above and below) is neotenous, it keeps its gills throughout its life.*

B Pengilley

Mudpuppies are mainly nocturnal, hiding during the day under stones or buried in the mud, but among dense weed they sometimes move about by day. They feed on worms, insect larvae, fish eggs, crayfishes, small fishes and frogs' eggs.

### Peter Pan salamanders

These salamanders are neotenous (see p 112); they never become fully adult but keep their gills throughout life. They do, however, become sexually mature. The size of the gills can vary. In cold, fresh water with plenty of oxygen the gills contract, but in warmer, more stagnant water low in oxygen they expand, becoming larger and more bushy so as to take up as much oxygen as possible. It is said that if the filaments of the plume-like gills become tangled the mudpuppy will rearrange them with its forefoot.

### Delayed spawning

Before going into a dormant state in winter, the mudpuppies mate, and a male and female may share the same hole in the bank. In the following spring the female lays 18–880 yellowish eggs, according to her size, each in its jelly envelope and $\frac{1}{4}$ in.

across. She sticks them one by one in a crowded group on the underside of a log or large stone or boulder in about 5 ft of water. Sometimes they are laid in a sandy hollow on the riverbed. She stays beside them until they hatch in 38–63 days according to the temperature of the water. As in all such instances, the warmer the water, to some extent, the less time the eggs take to hatch. It is usual to say that the female guards the eggs. Whether this is so or not has never been investigated, but despite their defenceless appearance mudpuppies can give a sharp nip when handled. When first hatched, they still have the yolk sac hanging from their underside. This lasts them until they are $1\frac{1}{2}$ in. long and about 2 months old, and able to find their own food. They mature in 5–7 years, at about 8 in. long and may live for 20 years.

## Whining like a puppy

Newts do have a larynx and European newts can make faint squeaks like the sound made by drawing a wet finger over glass. As these newts have lungs the sound is probably made by air driven from the lungs across the vocal cords. The lungless salamanders of California (p 1358) make a mouse-like squeak by contracting the throat and driving air either between the half-open jaws or through the nostrils. There is a legend that mudpuppies can bark like a dog. Perhaps this has arisen because when a mudpuppy is taken out of water it sometimes makes a sound like the whine of a puppy. If so, it would not be long before the story had grown to 'barking like a dog'

| class | **Amphibia** |
|---|---|
| order | **Caudata** |
| family | **Proteidae** |
| genus & species | *Necturus maculosus* |

# Mudskipper

*Mudskippers are fish which, instead of retreating with the falling tide, usually remain on the exposed mud. They can breathe air and move quickly over the mud, using their pectoral fins. Among some of the largest members of the goby family, they live on mud flats and mangrove swamps from West Africa to southeast Asia and the southwestern Pacific.*

*Mudskippers are 5—12 in. long, almost tadpole-like with a heavy head and long body compressed from side to side. They could well be described as pop-eyed, with their conspicuous eyes, placed well up on the head. These eyes can move*

## Three mud dwellers

Mudskippers show a zonation from the depths of the mangrove swamps, even up in the trees, through the mud of the forest floor down to the mid-tide level. There are three basic types of mudskippers. The eel-skippers *Scartelaos* so called because they have long slender bodies, live in the very soft mud at mid-tide level in the estuaries and are never far from water. Little is known of their habits. The second group, genus *Boleophthalmus*, live in large numbers on the mud at the seaward edge of mangrove forests. They may move into the margin of the forest, under the trees, but no more. They move their heads from side to side as they skitter over the mud skimming diatoms and algae from the surface. In a way not yet understood, they sort these

△ *Mudskipper profile: these are quite common in tropical parts of coastal Australia.*
◁ *Gill-chambers full of water, Malayan mudskippers* **Periophthalmus chrysopilos** *on mud.*

Jane Burton: Photo Res

*about in all directions. The front dorsal fin is high and spiny. The pectoral fins are fairly large and somewhat limb-like. The pelvic fins are joined to form a kind of sucker. The colour of the body varies from blue-grey to brownish, often with many small blue spots. The fins, especially the two dorsals, are decorated with coloured spots which vary according to the species.*

*In western Africa they live on the Saharan shores to the north and the Namibian shores to the south. In eastern Africa they range from East London to the Red Sea, and from there around the shores of the Indian Ocean and into the Indo-Australian region.*

out from the water in the mouth, swallow the diatoms and algae and spit out the water. The third group includes the genera *Periophthalmus* and *Periophthalmodon*, the commonest mudskippers, found along the banks of creeks and throughout the mangrove forests. These feed on insects that have fallen into the mud, on crabs, worms and the smaller mudskippers.

The species of *Periophthalmus* fall into two groups: those represented by *P. kalolo* in which the pelvic fins are still separate, and those represented by *P. chrysospilos* with the pelvic fins joined and forming a sucker. Mudskippers of the first group can climb only on to the exposed roots of mangroves whereas those of the second group are able to climb the vertical shoots and trunks by means of their suckers.

Harry & Claudy Frauca

▽▷ *In these Malayan species the pelvic fins have moved anterior to the pectoral fins and joined to form a sucker which enables them to climb the vertical trunks of mangroves.*

Jane Burton: Photo Res

## Living in air

All mudskippers spend much of their time out of water, but they constantly return to the pools left by the tide. The gill chambers are much enlarged to carry a supply of water but this has to be continually renewed in the pools although they can breathe air through the membranes lining the back of the mouth and the throat which are richly supplied with blood vessels. Mudskippers are said to dip their tails in water because they breathe through them. This is not so at all. They need to keep their skin moist, so they often splash water over themselves with one of the pectoral fins. They also have to keep their eyes moist. We have a supply of fluid on the surface of the eye supplied by the tear gland, and every time we blink we draw the lids over the eyes and

Jane Burton: Photo Res

moisten them. Fishes have no tear glands and a mudskipper cleans and moistens its eyes by pulling them back into the head.

## Double vision

The eyes themselves serve a dual purpose: the retina of the upper half is rich in rods, which means that it can detect small movements; the lower part has cones, which give colour vision. Presumably with the upper part of the eye they look down to detect insects and other small animals but watch other mudskippers for their colours, since these are used for signals. Eelskippers, when they meet, open their mouths at each other, showing the dark indigo blue inside. They also raise and lower the long spine of the dorsal fin. These movements are a challenge which may end in a pushing

match, after which the two separate.

Most, if not all, mudskippers have some form of signal which is often used while they are moving about over the mud. Usually it is a matter of raising and lowering the brightly coloured first dorsal fin every few seconds. One species throws itself in the air at frequent intervals, seeming to stand for a split second on the tip of its very thin tail before flopping back on the mud. This appears to be a matter of making those around keep off its territory, so all have their own feeding ground.

The mudskipper's pectoral fins are broad and mounted on a stubby limb, a sort of arm. In moving over the mud it uses these as crutches. It anchors its body with the anal fin and presses downwards and backwards with the pectoral fins, so it moves

with a similar action to a sealion. In the water it swims in the usual way, that is by wriggling its tail, usually keeping its head above water.

## Gymnastic courtship

Except in the breeding season, when the male has brighter colours, it is impossible to distinguish the male from the female except by dissection. At the breeding season in *Periophthalmus chrysopilos,* the only species whose breeding behaviour is at all well known, the colours of the male intensify and he has a brilliantly golden chin and throat. He displays this by doing 'press-ups' at passing females until he attracts one. She then follows him to his burrow. Mating seems to take place in the burrow, and the eggs are also laid there.

◁ *A giant mudskipper* **Periophthalmus** *displays by raising and lowering its dorsal and tail fin. This species lives on the banks of Malayan rivers where they dig 'castles' for themselves. This is a small pool with a muddy wall and perhaps a tunnel in the pool for the fish to retreat into. This species is about twice the size of* **Scartelaos** *being about 9 in. and also much fatter. It will sit on its 'castle' wall and defend its territory, evicting all rivals.*

▷ *Tail standing. This mudskipper* **Scartelaos viridis** *was filmed at the mouth of a small river near a Chinese hamlet in Malaya. It lives on the mud flat and is exposed only at very low tide. Every so often, as the series of frames show, it throws itself upwards until it is almost standing on its tail before flopping back onto the mud. This appears to be a matter of showing itself to warn those around to keep off its territory so all have a reasonable amount of feeding ground.*

## Mud sappers

Although it is generally believed that the first fishes to come on land, the ancestors of the salamanders, were probably of the coelacanth type (see p 481), the mudskippers show us some of the ways in which these ancestral land-water vertebrates must have lived. They are truly amphibious, some species spending most of their time on land, others most of their time in water, being able to stay submerged for up to 2 hours. They have overcome problems of breathing and movement on land, and have also solved the problem of shelters, by burrowing in the mud. The burrows are made up of a saucer-shaped depression leading into a vertical tunnel, with a rampart of mud round the saucer. The saucer may be anything from 6 in. to 2 ft across. One species makes a Y-shaped burrow with twin turrets of mud at the surface. The burrow is dug with the mouth, the fish bringing out mouthfuls of mud and spitting them on to the rampart to build it.

| class | **Pisces** |
| --- | --- |
| order | **Perciformes** |
| family | **Gobiidae** |

Film series by Jane Burton

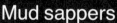

With a shell length of little more than 4 in. this tiny turtle, the common mud turtle, is one of the smallest water turtles of North America.

The common musk turtle has a much reduced plastron without hinges. The shields of the plastron are separated along the mid-line by soft skin.

# Mud turtle

The mud turtles and musk turtles of the family Kinosternidae are some of the smallest North American turtles: the adult eastern mud turtle has a brown or olive shell which is little more than 4 in. long. The young of this species has three ridges on the carapace, the upper part of the shell, but these disappear as it grows up. The plastron, or underpart of the shell, is light brown or yellow and the turtles have yellowish green spots on the head. The central part of the plastron is joined to the carapace while its front and rear portions are hinged to this central portion by strong connective tissues forming movable lobes. When the turtle withdraws its head, limbs and tail it draws these lobes over the openings, completely sealing itself in. Musk turtles are similar to mud turtles except that the plastron is very much smaller in proportion to the carapace and is hinged only in front, but the two kinds of turtles are alike in having musk glands along the sides of the body. The musk is much stronger in the musk turtles which are often called stinkpots as a result. Male mud turtles differ from females in having larger heads and longer tails and, when adult, their plastrons are concave. They also have patches of horny scales on the hindlegs, which are used to hold the female in mating.

There are about 17 species of mud turtle, 4 or 5 in the United States, and the rest in Central and South America. One large South American mud turtle has enlarged lobes on the plastron that make a perfect fit with the edges of the carapace, so the turtle inside is fully protected. The musk turtles live in the United States.

## Quiet life

Mud and musk turtles live in pools and sluggish streams where there are plenty of water plants. They crawl over the bottom and occasionally wander out over the land or bask on banks and tree stumps. The

Stinkpot—a three day old common musk turtle.

common musk turtle is rarely seen out of water but the keel-backed musk turtle of the southeastern United States often comes out to bask in the sun. The mud turtles are more likely to be found on land and they often live in very small pools and roadside ditches.

### An unpleasant catch

Mud turtles and musk turtles feed on tadpoles, snails, worms, water insects and fish. They also eat a large amount of carrion and are unpopular with anglers because they often take their bait. After giving an angler the impression that he has hooked a large fish the turtle adds insult to injury by discharging its foul-smelling musk when lifted from the water.

### Leisurely courtship

The courtship of mud turtles usually takes place in the water but the female comes on land to lay her eggs. To mate the male approaches the female from behind and noses her tail to confirm her sex. He then swims beside her, nudging her just behind her eye. She swims with him for some distance then stops suddenly. This is a signal for the male to climb onto her back, grasp the edges of her carapace with his toes and hold her tail to one side with the scaly patches on one of his hindlegs. Several fertile clutches may result from one mating and females isolated for 3—4 years have laid fertile eggs.

The eggs are laid under rotten logs and stumps or in nests dug in the earth. The musk turtles sometimes lay their eggs in muskrat nests. Up to 7 eggs with hard, brittle shells are laid in each clutch. They hatch in 60—90 days, depending on the heat provided by the sun and the decaying vegetation around them. The newly-hatched turtles have shells about 1 in. long. Males mature in 4—7 years and the females in 5—8 years. In captivity mud turtles have lived for 40 years but in the wild they fall prey to several predators; crows attack the adults, while king snakes, raccoons and skunks eat the eggs.

## The turtle frame

It is natural to assume that the plastron is no more than a breast plate to protect the underside of a turtle or tortoise, but in some species it is so small that it can offer very little protection. Even so, it still has an important part to play. In all turtles and tortoises the ribs are incorporated into the carapace and the plastron takes over to some extent the work of the ribs in bracing the body and in providing an anchoring surface for the muscles of the shoulders and hips. In the snapping turtle, for instance, in which the plastron is very much reduced, scientists have calculated that this small plastron is just sufficient to give the necessary strength and support to the body. It is much the same in the mud and musk turtles when they are young; they have a soft carapace and a rigid plastron which braces the carapace. As the turtles grow older and the carapace hardens the plastron is freed from this duty. Then it develops the hinges which, acting like lids, close over the turtle when it withdraws into its shell so giving it maximum protection.

| class | **Reptilia** |
| --- | --- |
| order | **Chelonia** |
| family | **Kinosternidae** |
| genera & species | ***Kinosternon subrubrum*** common mud turtle ***Sternotherus carinatus*** keel-backed musk turtle ***S. odoratus*** common musk turtle others |

# Mule deer

Mule deer of North America and the closely related white-tailed or Virginia deer are medium-sized deer, weighing up to 300 lb and standing up to nearly 4 ft at the shoulder. The does are about ⅓ smaller than the bucks. The hair is tawny or yellowish-brown in the summer, when the deer are said to be 'in the red', the winter coat is longer and greyer. The rump is white with a contrasting black-tipped tail. The antlers, grown in April or May and shed in January to March, distinguish the two species: the antlers of mule deer divide into two almost equal branches, the Virginia deer has similar antlers but

they are strangely curved forwards. Full size antlers are not grown until the fourth year, and a few years later they tend to become poorer. The Virginia deer can also be distinguished by its habit of carrying its all-white tail raised when running.

Mule deer live in the western parts of Canada and the United States, extending into northern Mexico. The Virginia deer is found in most parts of North America from southern Canada southwards. It is also found in Central America and northern South America. In British Columbia and the Pacific states of the United States there is a subspecies of the mule deer called the black-tailed deer. It is slightly smaller than the typical mule deer and the tail is completely black.

## Solitary deer

Mule deer and Virginia deer live in fairly open country and despite extensive hunting are more numerous now than when Europeans first settled in North America. This is due to the opening up of forests, so there are clearings providing plenty of food, with good cover nearby. The mule deer ranges farther into the mountains than the Virginia deer, spending the summer months on the slopes below the tree line where they browse the shoots and fresh twigs of trees such as pine and aspen. After the rut, which takes place in autumn, mule deer migrate down to the valleys where they feed on grasses, herbs and shrubs, often causing considerable damage to crops. They also eat mushrooms, nuts and lichens.

Unlike many other deer, mule deer and their relatives do not generally form herds

△ Unlike many deer, mule deer do not form herds although little groups such as this one are found.
▽ Unspoilt snow except for the track of a mule deer who wades belly deep through the white expanse.

▽ Independent young mule deer: after only 1 or 2 years the fawns fend for themselves.

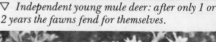

but live alone or in small family parties. In winter they will, however, gather in groups of up to 50 where food is easier to find. In these places they form 'yards', where the snow is trampled to expose food and trees are severely mutilated by browsing. When the supply at a 'yard' is exhausted the group searches for a new spot.

## Small harems

For most of the year the bucks are timid, living solitary lives in well-defined home ranges, but during the rut they become bold; they attack other bucks, pawing at the earth and butting each other. Each buck gathers a harem of up to four does. In June or July the does give birth to their fawns, usually twins. At first the fawns have dappled coats that are an excellent camouflage as the mother leaves them in dense under-growth where they lie motionless waiting for her to return to suckle them. This she does at regular intervals, about every 4 hours. After only a few days the fawns start to nibble on vegetation and by the sixth week they are weaned and follow their mother around. Also by this time, September, the fawns are losing their dappled coat and are growing a heavy winter coat. The young females may continue to follow their mother for 2 years but the males usually leave her sometime during the first year. The life span of a mule deer in the wild is about 10 years, but animals kept in captivity have lived for as long as 20 years.

## Much-hunted deer

Another reason for the North American deer's increase in population over the past century is that their natural enemies have been killed off. Although able to defend themselves with their hooves, mule deer fall prey to many predators. The fawns are the most vulnerable but many adults are killed in winter when they are weak from lack of food and deep snow slows them down. Bears, bobcats, pumas and coyotes all kill mule and Virginia deer and golden eagles take fawns, sometimes even adults.

Mule deer have always been hunted by man. Buckskin is made from their hide and their flesh is good to eat. Nowadays the deer are the target of thousands of weekend and holiday hunters who blaze away with such abandon that their activities are probably more dangerous to those taking part than to the deer. Accidents are common, and tales of farmers painting 'cow' on the flanks of their stock may be more than just tall stories.

△ *Dappled fawns nuzzle each other. Well-prepared for their fugitive life, they can walk from birth.*
▽ *Where wood and water meet: a Virginia deer doe breaks cover for a drink at the riverside.*

△ *Victim of an inquisitive nature — a big-eared doe with porcupine quills in her face.*

Fritz Siedel

*Canadian mountains provide a beautiful back cloth for pictures of mule deer—stag and doe above and stag in velvet below.*

Popperfoto

## The Kaibab plateau

Because of the economic value of their skins and meat, and the damage they cause to farms and forests, mule deer and Virginia deer are the subject of intensive control. In some places they are kept out by fences but in others they are encouraged by specially grown food plants. Nowadays the numbers are carefully regulated to keep them in harmony with the resources and needs of an area. Ways of regulating the numbers of deer have been learned slowly and the experiences on the Kaibab plateau in Arizona are a textbook example of failure to appreciate the factors affecting an animal's numbers.

The herd of mule deer on the Kaibab plateau was originally estimated at 4 000. Between 1905 and 1925 wolves were exterminated, several hundred pumas and several thousand coyotes were killed. As a result the deer increased rapidly. Just before 1920 the warning was given that there were so many deer that they were eating themselves out of food. A few years later the first fawns died of starvation. More warnings followed and by 1925 there were 100 000 mule deer on the plateau. A year later there were only 40 000; 60% had starved and numbers continued to drop over the following years. Attempts were made to reintroduce the food plants and numbers recovered, but there was another slump in 1954. By killing the predators there was no check on the population. In the 1920's Arizona game wardens actually arrested government hunters for attempting to reduce the population.

The Kaibab disaster is quite well known to biologists but less well known is the fact that the plateau is now a model of good game management. The different agencies cooperate and food plants are grown specially for the deer while the population is kept stable by carefully regulated hunting.

| class | **Mammalia** |
|---|---|
| order | **Artiodactyla** |
| family | **Cervidae** |
| genus & species | ***Odocoileus hemionus*** *mule deer* ***O. virginianus*** *Virginia deer* |

# Mullet

*Mullets are fish with elegantly elongated and compressed bodies covered with smooth scales. They are up to 2 ft long, even 3 ft in the striped mullet. Females are slightly longer than males. They have two short dorsal fins, the front one having 4 spines. The pelvic fins lie halfway along the underside, and the tail is somewhat forked. The mouth is small, somewhat narrow, and toothless except for a fringe of minute bristle-like teeth. Some of the mullets have an adipose eyelid; that is the skin over the eyeball is thickened with a fatty material and although still transparent it covers most of the outer surface of the eye, leaving only a small opening at the centre.*

*Mullets live in tropical and subtropical seas around the world and some move into temperate seas in summer. The 100 species of mullets are sometimes called grey mullets to distinguish them from the red mullets or surmullets (see goatfish p 904). Three species, the thicklipped, thinlipped and golden mullet, enter the coastal waters of the British Isles in early summer and leave again in autumn.*

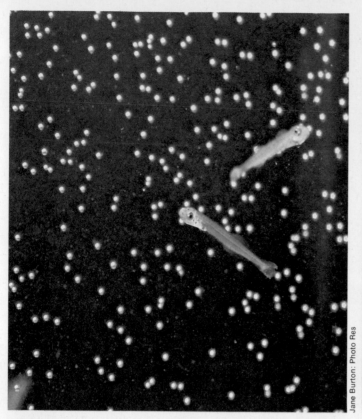

Jane Burton: Photo Res

## Sleeping on the sea bed

Although mullet swim in shoals, individual members dip down to the bottom from time to time to scoop up or suck up a mouthful of mud, spitting out the inedible part of the mud as they continue swimming. They also feed at the surface, with their mouths wide open, by sucking in small items of food. They do this especially where there is garbage and sewage, and will gather inshore as the tide is going out to pick up insects and grubs, particularly on the edges of beaches with piles of rotting seaweed.

At night the shoals break up and each mullet goes to its own spot on the bottom, the whole group well spread out but all facing the same way. At any disturbance they gather into shoals once more.

## Follow-my-leader fish

Rapid changes occur in the body system of mullets which enable them to go from salt to fresh water and back again, as they frequently swim into estuaries, often going considerable distances up rivers, usually with the tides. Exactly what these changes are is not known. In some parts of the world advantage is taken of this readiness to enter rivers and coastal lagoons. Walls are built across the entrances to narrow inlets with openings to let the small mullets in. The fish are then farmed, or cultivated in ponds. Mullet are difficult to catch on a hook as their lips tend to tear away as they struggle. and the usual way of catching them is with seine nets. In some places a tangle of net is placed on the outer side of the seine to prevent them jumping the nets. Mullet jump out of water holding their body rigid, in contrast with the curved body of, for example, a salmon leaping a weir. The moment one mullet jumps all the rest follow like sheep.

## All-round tasting

Mullets suck up sand and mud with their soft thick-lipped mouths and strain it through a sieve formed by numerous gill rakers, to extract the decomposed animal and vegetable matter. They will also eat small molluscs and scrape the fine filamentous green algae from the surfaces of stones and the piles of harbour and piers. Craig Phillips, in *The Captive Sea*, tells of a mullet in a seaquarium that cleaned a film of alga off the body of a manatee. They have taste buds, with which they find food, on the outer surface as well as inside the mouth. The food is ground to fine particles by a gizzard like that of a chicken. Its walls are so thick that the cavity inside, which is lined with a horny covering, is no more than a crack. The intestine is very long and closely coiled, a foot-long mullet having nearly 7 ft of intestine.

## Clustering to breed

Spawning is in shallow waters, the time of year varying with the species. The mullets cluster in tight pods, all touching each other. Little more is known of the breeding habits. Young mullets, an inch or more long, are found in tidal pools.

# Topsy-turvy fishes

From time to time there are reports of one mullet in an otherwise normal shoal swimming upside-down. These reports are usually received with scepticism but we have support for them in the notes published in 1953 by Dr Donald P de Sylva in the scientific journal *Copeia*. He saw, off the coast of Florida, a school of 15 mullet and one was swimming upside-down. At first he thought it was an albino and he tried to net it but as soon as he approached the school it reacted

◁△ *Not knowing which way to turn two very young grey mullet fry seem bewildered by the galaxy of bubbles surrounding them.*
△ *In the same predicament, slightly older fry stranded in a pool. Previous page: Grey mullet shoal in silhouette.*

in typical fashion by forming into a tight bunch which swam round and round him. The one fish continued to swim upside-down and at the same speed as the rest. This was on September 16, 1952. On October 10 of the same year, at another point off the Florida coast, Dr de Sylva saw a larger school, and this also had one member swimming upside-down. He followed the school for 5 minutes and at last the upside-down fish dropped back, apparently exhausted, and was netted. It was put into a freshwater aquarium but died some hours later, perhaps from having been transferred so suddenly from salt to fresh water. A post mortem showed no injury, sickness or disease.

It is usually assumed that upside-down fish are sick or dead, except for a catfish *Synodontis batensoda*, living in the Nile and other African rivers, which always does so, and its belly is coloured while its back is light. But there is a record of a school of blue runners *Caranx fusus*, one of the jacks of the family Carangidae, chasing anchovies, and all were swimming upside-down.

| class | **Pisces** |
|---|---|
| order | **Perciformes** |
| family | **Mugilidae** |
| genus & species | *Crenimugil labrosus* thicklipped grey mullet *Liza auratus* golden mullet *L. ramada* thinlipped grey mullet others |

# Multimammate rat

The name multimammate rat is derived from the unusual number of teats—up to 18 pairs—on the females, which lie on the chest and belly between armpits and groin. Most multimammate rats have 8—10 pairs but even this is considerably more than the normal maximum of 5 pairs found in other rats and mice. The multimammate rat looks like the ship or black rat. The soft fur is dark grey or brown above and paler below. The head and body are 4—6 in. long and the tail is slightly shorter. The feet, especially the forefeet, are small.

This rodent, sometimes known as the multimammate mouse has features of both rats and mice as well as certain features which are unique. As a result the multimammate rat has sometimes been classed scientifically with the rats, genus **Rattus,** the mice, genus **Mus** or in a genus of its own **Mastomys.** Nowadays it is classed as a rat. Multimammate rats are one of the commonest rodents in Africa. They can be found from Morocco to the Cape of Good Hope and from east to west coasts. They are absent only from deserts, dry plains and mountains.

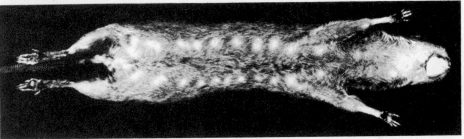

*An ordinary rat with a difference, for the multimammate rat (top) has 8—10 pairs, sometimes even up to 18 pairs, of teats. What is your estimate for the museum specimen (bottom)? As there may be up to 20 babies in one litter the purpose of this rather unique feature becomes obvious.*

## Borrowed burrows

Originally multimammate rats lived in open savannah or marshy country but like house mice, common rats and ship rats they have learnt to live with humans. They are found in barns and outhouses and also in lofts, for they are good climbers and in captivity can climb dangling strings. Where food is plentiful it is possible for both these rats and mice to live together, the multimammate rats being very tolerant of their own kind and of others. The multimammate rats are driven out, however, if food becomes short. In the wild they usually live in the abandoned burrows of other small animals and several families may be found living harmoniously in one burrow. When no burrows are available they dig their own holes, but they are weak diggers and have to use ground that is soft or cracked. In captivity they can be induced to dig tunnels by sprinkling water on a tray of sand to simulate rain.

## Pests of crops

Multimammate rats are mainly vegetarian and when they live in fields of crops or in warehouses they can become severe pests, the damage they cause being accentuated by their habit of hoarding food. In East Africa they feed on maize from April to May, then transfer their attentions to sorghum in July and August. After that they attack cotton crops, climbing the plants to eat the seeds and unopened fruit and at the same time soiling the lint.

As in lemmings, voles and other rodents, there are sometimes plagues of multimammate rats that do untold damage to crops. It is not known for certain why these plagues occur but it is known that under certain conditions, for example, when food from farm crops is plentiful, the population

of these rats is vastly increased and rats from neighbouring areas flood in to swell the numbers.

## Exploding populations

Multimammate rats first breed when 3 months old and the babies are born after a 3-week gestation. The male lives with the female and after the babies are born he stands guard at the entrance to the burrow. Nesting burrows are more extensive than those used at other times and they are kept clean by pushing out droppings and refuse. There may be up to 20 babies in one litter but usually the number is nearer 10. At first they are sparsely covered with hair and are blind for a fortnight. They can fend for themselves when 19 days old, but they stay in the nest for a longer period, even though their mother may have another litter within 25 days of their birth.

At the end of the dry season a population of multimammate rats is at a low level but by the end of the wet season they may be present in plague proportions because of the large litters that are produced in rapid succession during times of plenty. During the peak of breeding the population can expand five times each month.

Multimammate rats are preyed on by many enemies, including civets, genets, owls, eagles and snakes but when their numbers are high, as in plague years, it is doubtful whether these predators have any appreciable effect on their numbers.

## Important rodent

The high rate of reproduction in multimammate rats brings dangers of two kinds of plague. First there is the straightforward plague of rats that causes damage to standing crops and stored food, then there is the

danger of bubonic plague which these rats carry. They are particularly dangerous because they associate with man, carrying the plague germs from the reservoir of plague in wild rodents to human habitations. On several occasions a plague of multimammate rats has led to an epidemic of bubonic fever. As a result multimammate rats have been kept in the laboratory for research into plague cures. Great care has to be taken to make sure that they do not escape in countries where there is no plague, as they can chew through the walls of aluminium cages. In the United States, for example, multimammate rats are kept only in the east, because there are semi-dry regions in the west similar to regions in southern Africa where they thrive. If they were to get free in the western United States they could easily form a link between the wild reservoir of plague and man.

Multimammate rats are also susceptible to bilharzia, a parasitic fluke, and they readily develop stomach cancers. Man also suffers from these, and studies on the multimammate rat may help fight both afflictions.

| class | **Mammalia** |
|---|---|
| order | **Rodentia** |
| family | **Muridae** |
| genus & species | *Rattus natalensis* |

# Muntjac

Muntjac are among the most primitive of deer. They are small, standing only 16—25 in. at the shoulder although somewhat higher at the rump. The males have long, tusk-like upper canines and only very small antlers on top of their long hairy bases (pedicels). The pedicels themselves continue down onto the face, often converging in a V and this has given rise to the alternative name of rib-faced deer. The females have no antlers and the short pedicels are just bony knobs covered with tufts of hair.

True muntjac have antlers up to 1 ft long, usually branched at the base and with a large burr, and they have large glands on the face. The Indian muntjac of India, Burma and Thailand to Indonesia is up to 22 in. high with a reddish coat. The Pleihari muntjac is smaller with a yellower coat and un-branched antlers. This lives alongside a race of the Indian muntjac in Borneo. The Chinese muntjac, which ranges as far north as the Yangtze River, is similar to the Pleihari but is even smaller and has smaller face glands. The closely related tufted deer has very short antlers and weaker pedicels which do not converge. Usually the antlers are so short that they do not go beyond the long tuft of reddish hair on the forehead. Tufted deer, which have no face glands; live in China over the same range as the Chinese muntjac. Their coat is grey to brown, they have long lateral hoofs and are 25 in. high.

Although the true muntjacs and tufted deer differ in some respects there are two forms of muntjac which bridge the gap. These are Fea's muntjac of Burma and the hairy-fronted muntjac of the Ningpo district in China, which look like tufted deer with long antlers and they also have strong 'ribs' on the face. So far we have little information about these two but they are important because they show the close relation between the tufted deer of China and the true muntjacs.

## Twilight browsers

Muntjac are solitary. They live in forest and bush in hilly country—in the Himalayas and Szechwan they go up to 8 000 ft. By day they lie up in thickets, going out in the late evening to feed and again, very often, in the early morning. They move slowly and cautiously, frequently pausing and standing still, but they can dash away with quick bounds when alarmed. All muntjac have well developed senses, especially of smell and hearing.

They feed on the open hillside on herbs, grass and soft wood, and also the tender parts of the bushes. Tufted deer and Fea's muntjac live in more mountainous country and in Szechwan the local blackish race of tufted deer go up to the tree-line at 10 000 ft. Both are browsers rather than grazers, feeding especially on soft woods, such as

▽ *The cry of the hunted. A male Chinese muntjac pauses momentarily to sound the alarm warning all the other deer in the area of the impending danger. If his predator does not catch him, there will be little else to catch as all the other animals will have been alerted by his frequent barks.*

Geoffrey Kinns

poplar, willow and birch. They are also solitary and each has its own territory. Like true muntjacs they are shy, going out only at twilight to feed.

## Deer that mew

The female makes shrill mewing sounds during the breeding season, and the male makes a belling bark. The breeding season is towards the end of summer, earlier than in other deer. Gestation is 6 months, the young being born in late winter or very early spring. It is not known whether the males fight at this time or whether they just form pairs with females or gather harems. The distress call of the fawn is a mew very like the females' mewing call.

## Barking predator-alarm

When a predator is far enough away not to pose a direct threat a muntjac barks its warning. This is unusual in a solitary animal, as it is presumably a warning call to others around. Because of the bark the deer is known locally as *Kakur*, in imitation of its call, or simply barking deer. The bark may be heard for miles and may be kept up for half an hour, completely ruining the chance of a tiger or leopard catching anything else, since all small animals for miles around are alerted by it. When chased, muntjac also bark, at half minute intervals, going on and on for as long as the chase lasts. When startled or excited they make a rattling sound from the throat, or perhaps by chattering their teeth. When hiding, muntjacs stand motionless with their necks stretched forward and downward. When actually threatened or brought to bay they bark, stamp their front hoofs on the ground and move back a few steps ready to defend themselves. Their chief predators are leopard, tiger, hyaena, wolf and eagle. Whether muntjac try to defend themselves against larger enemies is not known but they have been seen to attack dogs with their tusks and horns. The Szechwan tufted deer, living in thick forest, merely runs for 500 yd or so, then stops and begins to feed again. Its main enemy is the wolf.

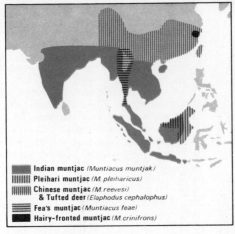

Indian muntjac *(Muntiacus muntjak)*
Pleihari muntjac *(M. pleiharicus)*
Chinese muntjac *(M. reevesi)* & Tufted deer *(Elaphodus cephalophus)*
Fea's muntjac *(Muntiacus feae)*
Hairy-fronted muntjac *(M. crinifrons)*

△ *Muntjac are among the most primitive deer. The half a dozen species are usually found in areas of dense vegetation and hilly ranges from sea level to medium elevations. In certain areas of their distribution they are hunted by natives for their meat and skins.*

▽ *A personal enquiry. A male Chinese muntjac sniffs tentatively at a female.*

▽ *Years of worry—or merely growth? The bony pedicels extend down onto the face like ribs, and the long dark slit openings of the face glands are prominently marked.*

Jane Burton: Photo Res

G Rüppell

▽ *Not just a taste organ: Chinese muntjac uses an extremely long tongue to clean its eye.*

Peter Livesley

# Chinese deer in England

In 1900, the 11th Duke of Bedford liberated some Indian muntjac into the countryside around Woburn. He soon regretted his action, however, when they proved rather aggressive towards small dogs, so he tried to kill them off and introduced the smaller, less pugnacious Chinese muntjac to take their place. In this he was successful, and some of the muntjac that live in England today are the result of interbreeding between the Indian and Chinese species, but most are Chinese. They have spread very widely, but being solitary animals they have not built up very large numbers. A few years ago it was estimated by GK Whitehead that there were between 400 and 1000 living wild in England. In Bedfordshire, where they have been longest established, they are commonest in the woods around Ampthill and Luton; but they are found right up to and across the Northamptonshire border, round such places as Whittlebury, Silverstone, Towcester and Daventry. In 1952 muntjac were first recorded in the Forest of Dean in Warwickshire. In 1954 they were seen near Rugby and in 1955, south of Birmingham. They also occur in Hertfordshire around Bricketwood, St Albans, Bishop's Stortford and Hertford; they have once been recorded in Middlesex, when in 1958 one was caught in Enfield behind somebody's garage; it was released in the nearby Epping Forest (Essex) but has not been seen since. Muntjac are sporadically reported in Essex, Cambridgeshire, Norfolk, Huntingdonshire and Buckinghamshire; they have recently turned up, and are said to be not uncommon, in Oxfordshire near Bicester, Thame and in the southwestern Chilterns, and near Henley and Maidenhead in Berkshire. Like the sika and Chinese water-deer, the muntjac is now well established in England and is there to stay.

| class | **Mammalia** |
|---|---|
| order | **Artiodactyla** |
| family | **Cervidae** |
| genera & species | **Muntiacus crinifrons** *hairy-fronted muntjac* |
| | **M. feae** *Fea's muntjac* |
| | **M. muntjak** *Indian muntjac* |
| | **M. pleiharicus** *Pleihari muntjac* |
| | **M. reevesi** *Chinese muntjac* |
| | **Elaphodus cephalophus** *tufted deer* |

△ *Caught napping. These roosting muscovy ducks are very much at home as they are tree ducks by nature. Their native home is on water in well wooded areas.*

# Muscovy duck

*The muscovy duck is no more connected with Russia than turkeys are with Turkey. The name is derived from muskduck. A muscovy duck is between a duck and a goose in size and is among the ugliest of birds. The naked skin of the face is bright red and thrown into a knoblike caruncle, which is more developed in the male than in the female. The male also has a mane-like crest. The plumage is usually dark green, almost black, with patches of white, and the legs are lead blue. Altogether they have the appearance of being scruffy and unkempt. In captivity several colour varieties have been bred: domestic muscovy ducks may be blue, brown or white, with yellow or orange legs. One variety is white with a black crest. Wild muscovies are smaller and have smaller caruncles than the domestic varieties.*

*The original home of the muscovy duck is in tropical America, from Mexico to Peru and Argentina. It has been introduced to many parts of the world, especially to warmer regions where it thrives—more so than domestic mallards.*

### Mystery ducks

In their native home muscovy ducks are found on streams, lakes and marshes that are surrounded by woods and forests, for they are tree ducks, roosting and nesting well above the ground. At one time they were common but their numbers have diminished through persecution. They were domesticated by the South American Indians long before the Spanish Conquistadores arrived. The Spaniards took domestic muscovy ducks to Europe where they thrived despite the colder climate. Their strange appearance is attractive to some people and they are kept as ornamen-

△ *A buxom mother muscovy proudly guards her chicks. Muscovies are fatter when domesticated.*

tal waterfowl. One reason for their popularity is that their need for a stretch of water on which to swim is less than that of other ducks. Muscovies are also kept for their flesh although this is not as good as that of the mallard. The practice is, however, to cross muscovies with domestic mallards. The sterile hybrids grow fast and their flesh is good to eat.

Domestic muscovies sometimes become wild and establish themselves on lakes or canals. As a result there are often reports of strange water birds that defy identification with a pocket birdbook. The black and white patchwork plumage and red, bloated face are, however, sufficiently distinctive.

Muscovy ducks feed mainly on plants but they also eat animals such as small fish, crabs, insects and worms.

### Unwilling mates

Outside the breeding season muscovy ducks live in flocks of 50 or more. The males are promiscuous, mating with any female that is ready to lay and keeping other males away. They fight fiercely with their bills and the well developed claws on their feet, and also batter each other with their wings, which are armed with bony knobs on the 'elbows'. Muscovies have a rather comical display. They nod their heads back and forth in abrupt jerks with their necks outstretched and crests raised. The female has a rather similar display and pairs of muscovies can be seen standing side by side nodding their heads to and fro and quietly hissing to each other. Mating is rather abrupt; the male chases the female and tries to grab her. At first she tries to escape and they may run about for some time before she submits.

The nest is built in a hole in a tree and all the raising of the young is done by the female. Brown and yellow ducklings hatch out after 35 days. They leave the nest in the tree while still very young and are escorted to the waters' edge by their mother.

▽ *A bundle of fluffy brothers and sisters cuddle together until their mother returns.*

1503

William S Paton

△ *Not to be lightly interfered with. An ugly looking gentleman with his red, hairless face and caruncle, shaggy crest and vicious beak.*
▷ *Follow-my-leader on the duck pond.*

# Muscovite sees red

Domestic muscovy ducks are quite tame yet some owners have found to their cost that red clothing can have the same effect on a muscovy duck as the proverbial waving red rag has on a bull. First the male muscovy wags his tail from side to side and fluffs out his feathers, so he looks much bigger. At the same time he begins his head nodding and hissing routine which is a warning to a rival that something more will happen if he does not retreat. The same goes for a human wearing red; if he does not retreat, the muscovy advances with his crest rising and falling, and stabbing with his closed beak. The blows which fall on the level of the knees, are usually sufficient to cause a rapid retreat; otherwise the third phase of the attack starts. The muscovy spreads his wings to the ground, curls his claws in until the webs of his feet are clear of the ground, and flies at the head of the offending person, clawing and beating with his wings. The claws inflict deep scratches and the muscovy also takes beakfuls of flesh, squeezing and tearing it.

It seems that in those instances of apparently unprovoked attacks, the male muscovy has mistaken an article of red clothing for the red skin on a rival duck. To us it is ridiculous that a duck's head and a red sweater can be confused, but the bird is merely reacting to the colour, and not the shape, in the same way as a male robin attacks a bunch of red feathers placed in his territory. Although it does not look like a real robin it conveys the same meaning as a red breast.

| class | **Aves** |
|-------|----------|
| order | **Anseriformes** |
| family | **Anatidae** |
| genus & species | *Cairina moschata* |

Barnaby's

1504

# Musk-deer

Musk-deer are the most primitive living members of the deer family Cervidae and because of this the Russian scientist Flerov has separated them into the family Moschidae on their own. Musk-deer have no antlers or face glands but both sexes have a gland under the tail that gives out a substance with a goaty smell. The adult males have a pouch on the abdomen which secretes a pungent jelly-like musk. Both male and female have long upper canines, those of the male being up to 4 in. long, sabre-like and curving backwards. They are also movable, being pulled upright in the jaw by a band of muscle when the animal opens its mouth.

The largest of the three species, the Siberian musk-deer, has a brownish dappled coat with very long hair reaching 4 in. on the rump. It has slender legs and stands up to 22 in. at the shoulder, the rump being higher. The mountain musk-deer of the Himalayas and the borders of the Tibetan plateau is smaller, uniformly coloured light grey, and has short stout legs and a long face. The dwarf musk-deer is dark grey, 16—18 in. high, has very stout limbs and a short face. The mountain and dwarf species live in adjacent areas with slightly overlapping ranges. The first lives above the tree-line at 8—16 000 ft and the second lives in the forest zone at 5—10 000 ft. Some zoologists consider these two forms to be subspecies of the single species but they are being treated as two separate species here.

## Strongly territorial

During the day the solitary, territorial musk-deer hide up in thickets or rest between boulders, going out only at twilight or after nightfall. They progress by leaps and bounds, scrambling up steep slopes with ease, their long lateral hoofs or dew claws preventing them from slipping. They can swim well and can move over snow fairly easily because of their spreading hoofs. Apart from this their behaviour varies in different parts of their range. In Siberia the musk-deer live in the middle part of the mountain taiga. In winter they live mainly in the fir and spruce forests on the steepest slopes where less snow settles. Each territory has a rocky outcrop at its centre which is used as a refuge from predators and in country where there are few rocks, the musk-deer are also few in number. In summer the deer wander down into river valleys with good grass and other herbage and where the trees are scattered, but they avoid swampy forest. At all times the males are found higher up than the females. When the deer return to the slopes in winter they set up new territories, each about a square mile in area, with the territory of the buck usually next to one belonging to a doe. Each buck has a marking-spot in his territory which he constantly visits, marking it with both musk and droppings. These marking-spots, recognisable by their smoothness, are small, thick dead branches, rhododendron stalks, willow or other soft wood and are never very far off the ground. The mountain musk-deer keep their territories all the year round, but they also fight over them, like the Siberian musk-deer, slashing each other with their tusks, causing deep neck wounds, but these never seem to be fatal.

▽ *A lone Siberian musk-deer bounds into the evening sun. These shy, solitary creatures do not come out into the open until evening.*

Geoffrey Kinns: AFA

### Feeding like reindeer

In winter when there is thin snow on the ground musk-deer scrape it away to get at the mosses, lichens, grass and leaves underneath. When it is too deep they scrape the the lichens off the trees, pull up young shoots or even eat pine needles. They sometimes climb up the leaning trunks of trees to feed or to take refuge at the top, their iron-hard hoofs making nicks in the bark. Musk-deer are fond of salt-licks.

### Slow to grow up

The breeding season begins in December and ends in January, much later than in true deer. The males fight among themselves with their tusk-like canine teeth, the fights sometimes ending fatally. They round up females into their territories, marking these territories liberally with musk. Before rounding her up the male chases a female, sometimes for as long as 24 hours, until she is exhausted and tries to hide under a thicket or among boulders. This chasing is known as the 'run'. Mating may take place either during it or at the end of it. Gestation is 190 days and the young are born between April and June. The Siberian and dwarf musk-deer usually have twins, but the mountain species usually just have a single young at a time. The fawns remain hidden among rocks or in bushes until they are ready to follow their mothers. When danger threatens, the female walks away from where the young is hidden, even feigning weakness or sickness, and when the predator chases her, she hides between rocks or up a steep slope. The fawns become more or less full-sized between 15 and 17 months and sexually mature after 3 years. The newly-born fawn has a coat of reddish transverse stripes and whitish longitudinal stripes which is replaced by a dappled coat at the end of 6 months. This dappled coat is shed after 3 years except in the Siberian species which remains dappled in the adult.

### Ringed by hazards

Adult musk-deer are killed by yellow-throated marten, dhole, lynx, wolf, leopard, snow leopard, bear and wolverine, although the male tries to defend himself with his tusk-like canines. Eagles and foxes kill the fawns. In summer the deer are pestered by gnats and mosquitoes, and botflies lay their eggs under their skin where the bot larvae develop. Possibly because they have so many enemies musk-deer are extremely shy and they sleep very lightly as hunters discover as soon as they try to get within shooting distance. At the slightest disturbance, the deer spring up on all four legs at once and bound off, bouncing like a rubber ball for about 100 yd, when they stop and look back at their pursuers.

## Deer perfume

The musk-deer is the most coveted wild animal of China and Siberia, mainly for its thick, oily, rather jelly-like musk, which is red but becomes black as it dries. When first extracted it has an obnoxious odour but as it dries it gives off a pleasant scent. Each musk pod contains about an ounce of musk. Oriental musk, from the dwarf musk-deer, is more valuable than 'Kabardinic' the

musk from the Siberian species. It is used for perfumes and, in China, as an aphrodisiac and fertility drug, and to alleviate pain. In Tibet it is mixed with sheep-dung and Chinese tobacco and taken as snuff. Other parts of the musk-deer are valuable as well: fine leather is made from the skin, and the flesh is favoured by Tibetans although Russians and Chinese tend to find it tasteless and too musky.

Musk-deer are still hunted for their musk, but not as much as formerly. During the 1930's, 10–15 000 musk-deer were killed annually, bringing in a total of £100 000. The usual way of catching them is to set up a noose and jerk-snare. It is, however, not necessary to kill the animal to extract the musk. A tube can be put into the opening of the sac, and a slight pressure squirts the stream of musk into the tube. The Russian zoologist Konstantin Flerov has suggested that a profitable industry might be started by farming musk-deer.

| class | **Mammalia** |
|---|---|
| order | **Artiodactyla** |
| family | **Moschidae** |
| genus & species | *Moschus berezovskii* dwarf musk-deer *M. chrysogaster* mountain musk-deer *M. moschiferus* Siberian musk-deer |

▽ *A Siberian musk-deer with its feet firmly on the ground. They have spreading hoofs, with long dew claws, which help to stop them slipping as they bound over rocky terrain.*

# Musk-ox

*The musk-ox lives in the bleak hostile arctic tundra of Canada and Greenland. Its scientific name **Ovibos moschatus,** literally 'musky sheep-ox', is something of a misnomer as it is neither a sheep nor an ox but occupies a position intermediate between sheep and goats on the one hand and sheep and cattle on the other. Although physically it resembles cattle, it is probably more nearly related to sheep and goats and, indeed, is sometimes called the musk-sheep. The strong musky odour, confined to bulls in rut, is emitted from musk glands on the face and detectable even at a distance of*

*100 yd. The closest living relative of the musk-ox is the takin, of the mountainous regions of Tibet, Burma and China.*

*The bull musk-ox is massive, standing 5 ft at the shoulder, which carries a slight hump, and it weighs up to 700 lb; the cows are nearly as large. The legs are short and sturdy with broad hoofs, and bulls have musk glands on the face. The horns, joined at their bases in the centre of the head, grow sideways and downwards and then curve back until the tips are level with the bases. The musk-ox has a dense woolly undercoat which is impervious to cold and damp, and a shaggy dark-brown mantle of long guard hairs, reaching almost to the ground in winter. Protected by this immense coat it can withstand the worst Arctic weather. Its range, extends from Arctic Canada to the extreme northern tip of Ellesmere Island.*

## Snow their enemy

The surface soil in the musk-oxen's arctic territory scarcely thaws, even in summer, while the average January temperature is 34°C/30°F below zero and only a few degrees higher in February. Temperatures can drop to 56°C/70°F below zero and storms last for days. The musk-oxen, however, do not seek shelter in bad weather but remain on the exposed, wind-lashed slopes, where the scant vegetation upon which they feed is less likely to be buried by snow. They live in herds 20–30 strong, sometimes up to 100, and during the worst blizzards huddle together, backs to the wind, sheltering the calves in the centre of the herd. Exceptionally adverse weather can, however, bring disaster even to these hardy animals. In the winter of 1953–1954 large numbers died from starvation in parts of Greenland when unusually heavy and prolonged snowfalls covered their feeding grounds.

## Slow breeders

During the rut, the bulls fight for possession of the herds and the battles are primitive and awe-inspiring. As a strange bull approaches a herd the lead bull will go forward slowly to meet him. As if at a signal, the two great beasts charge, their foreheads, protected by the flattened bases of their horns, crashing together with a crack that can be heard over a mile away. The charge is repeated until one or the other capitulates. Vanquished bulls are driven away and become solitary wanderers. In the rutting season bulls become so jealous of their cows that they will charge even at birds which alight too near them.

The breeding rate is slow; cows do not mature until their fourth or fifth year and

then calve only every other year, unless their calf is lost in its early months. Mating takes place in August and the single calf is born in the following April or May when the temperature is seldom more than 29°C/20°F below zero. The calf has a thick woolly coat and can follow its mother when only an hour old. Within a week it begins to nibble at plants but it remains with its mother for at least 18 months. The life span is up to 20 years.

## Success and failure of the phalanx

Although the musk-ox is swift and agile, even in snow, it does not flee when attacked. Wolves are the main natural enemy and a herd of musk-oxen threatened by a pack of wolves forms a phalanx, cows and calves in the centre, bulls on the outside facing the attackers. Individual wolves are gored or trampled; or the packs of wolves are driven off by a combined charge. This method of defence has, however, brought the musk-ox close to extinction when used against men. Eskimos have always hunted it, using the

△ *Stepping it up. Three massive musk oxen careering through the snow.*

long guard hairs to make mosquito nets, carving ladles and spear-heads from the horn and eating the meat which is said to resemble beef. Their primitive weapons had little effect on the numbers, estimated at over a million, which roamed the arctic tundra before the middle of the last century: but men with guns were a different matter.

When whalers from Scotland and New England hunting the bowhead, or arctic right whale, began to winter in Hudson Bay, the herds that stood still in the face of guns provided an easy way to provision ships and thousands of musk-oxen were shot for meat. Later, musk-ox robes became a valuable trading item. Between 1862 and 1916 the Hudson Bay Company alone bought 15 000 and arctic explorers came to depend largely upon the musk-ox for survival, between them killing more than 1 000 on Ellesmere Island in the years from 1880 to 1917. Later still musk-ox calves were in demand by zoological gardens throughout the world so the remaining herds were decimated, as the only way of capturing calves at that time was to shoot all the adults in a herd so that the unprotected calves could easily be netted. In face of the armed hunters the musk-oxen formed their phalanx, as they did against wolves, but even when one had been shot the hunter could not take the carcass because the rest of the herd charged whenever he went near it.

## Musk-ox now protected

By 1917, as a result of indiscriminate slaughter, the musk-ox had become so rare that the Canadian government ordered its complete protection. Since then, it has made a slow but steady recovery on Canadian territory and later various measures were undertaken to ensure its continued existence, and to try to increase its range. In 1929, 18 were transferred from Greenland to Spitzbergen where they have now increased to about 100. The following year 34 Greenland musk-oxen were released on Nunivak Island, off Alaska; in 1962, 340 were counted there. There is also a herd of about 30 in the Dovrefjell mountains in Norway. All these introduced musk-oxen have been completely protected from the date of introduction, and those on Greenland have been protected since 1951.

Recovery is slow, and any redistribution of the animals is a long and difficult task because they have to be taken in the wild state and transported to their new feeding grounds. It has been demonstrated that it is impracticable to raise musk-oxen in any numbers in captivity, and only a very few have ever been reared, under the most attentive and expert care, in zoos.

In the spring of 1967 the Northwest Territories Council decided, against the advice of government biologists, to permit the shooting of 32 musk-oxen a year, at a price of $4 000 per head. There was considerable public opposition, however, to this scheme and in October 1967 the Council abandoned the whole idea. Even the hunters agreed that they were not missing much 'sport'. As Vilhjalmur Stefansson put it 'I would say that equally good sport could be secured with far less trouble and expense by paying some farmer for the permission of going into his pasture and killing his cows'. Freed at last from the menace of man's destructive pastimes the musk-ox is gradually regaining the former extent of its range. It could play a tremendous part in the economy of the north, for it thrives well in these barren parts. CHL Clarke, in *A Biological Investigation of the Thelon Game Sanctuary* points out that 'no animal could be more easily herded and the value of a properly utilised carcass would be considerable. . . The live animal might be comparable to the yak as a pack or saddle beast'.

| class | **Mammalia** |
|---|---|
| order | **Artiodactyla** |
| family | **Bovidae** |
| genus & species | *Ovibos moschatus* |

▽ *Out in the cold. A young musk-ox fends for itself while the sun still shines. When the weather becomes severe it will huddle in the centre of a group for warmth and protection.*

▷△ *Weathered Arctic travellers. Their long, thick shaggy coats together with their waterproof undercoats are adequate protection from the snow and icy winds.*

▷▽ *Arctic hippies? At the photographer's approach these musk-oxen begin to form into their protective phalanx with the cows and calves at the centre.*

Photos by Fred Bruemmer

# Muskrat

*The muskrat is a large vole with a head and body length of 9—12 in. and a tail of 7—11 in. The name is derived from the secretions of two glands at the base of the tail. The fur colour ranges from silvery brown to almost black. Under the long, coarse guard hairs there is a short, dense layer of very soft hair. The short undercoat is very hardwearing and is sold under the name of musquash, the name given to the animal by Canadian Indians.*

*Muskrats are adapted to an aquatic life. The scaly, almost hairless tail is flattened from side to side so acting as a rudder. The hindfeet are partly webbed and fringed with short, stiff hairs.*

*The two species are native to North America. The Newfoundland muskrat is restricted to that island, while the other species ranges widely over the mainland from Alaska and Labrador southwards to Baja California and South Carolina. Muskrats have been introduced to several parts of Europe.*

## Two kinds of nests

The presence of muskrats in an area, is shown by well-defined channels through the vegetation, slides down banks and by networks of tunnels. They are usually found away from water only when they are searching for new feeding grounds. They live in marshes, lakes and rivers, preferably where there is dense vegetation that provides them with both food and cover. Muskrats make two types of nest: in open swamps a pile of water vegetation is made, perhaps 4 ft high and 5 ft across. The walls are cemented with mud and a nest of finely shredded leaves is made in the middle. Several tunnels connect the nest with underwater exits. The other type of nest is built along the edges of ponds and rivers, where muskrats dig elaborate tunnels to a nest above the high water mark. The entrances are either underwater, below the level of the thickest ice, or above water, when they are camouflaged by piles of vegetation.

Muskrats can stay underwater for up to 12 minutes. Normally they dive for shorter periods, only staying submerged when danger threatens. In the winter they keep open breathing holes in the ice by continually breaking the ice as it forms. As the ice around the hole thickens it is plugged with plants giving the muskrat shelter from the sight of enemies when it surfaces to breathe.

## Water plants feeder

The food of muskrats consists mainly of roots and leaves of water plants such as water lilies, wild rice, cattails and arrowheads. In winter they do not feed on stored food but on the roots of water plants which they grub out from the mud. Crops such as maize, alfalfa, clover and peanuts are plundered and also some animal food is eaten, such as crayfish, mussels, and occasionally fish.

## Rapid breeding

In the northern parts of their range, muskrats breed from spring to autumn and several families are raised in that time. In the south breeding continues all the year round, with a peak of births from November to April. Gestation lasts only 22—30 days and the young muskrats are only 2—3 in. long when born. There are usually 5—7 in a litter. They are blind, naked and helpless at birth, and are weaned when one month old, although they will have started nibbling plants some time previously. When they are weaned the mother drives them out of the nest because she has mated shortly after they were born and will soon give birth to another litter of rats.

## Floods are dangerous

Muskrats are particularly vulnerable during floods, and are more common in lakes and rivers that are not susceptible to flooding. As the muskrats are driven from their nests they seek refuge on rafts of floating vegetation and on trees where bark and twigs form an emergency food. Fighting is common under these conditions and many muskrats die of drowning, disease and cold. The lack of cover and the weakened con-

dition of the muskrats also makes them an easy target for their many predators, which include red-tailed hawks, great horned owls, bald eagles, foxes, coyotes and raccoons. In the water they are attacked by alligators, snapping turtles, pike and water snakes such as the water moccasin. Perhaps their worst enemy is the mink, but it probably only kills the excess population, that is the young and sick. The American naturalist Paul Errington in his book *On Predation and Life,* has described vividly the limitations on muskrat overpopulation: 'Life among the muskrats proved to be a most hectic succession of fights, evictions, trespasses, abandonments of litters, and other troubles. Young animals died of a skin disease. . . They were preyed upon by minks. They were eaten by cannibalistic members of their own kind.'

## Friend or foe?

Muskrat fur is very valuable. Each year pelts worth tens of millions of dollars are traded in North America. For this reason alone the muskrat is a very useful animal, but they are also welcomed in many places as they keep waterways open by eating water plants. They are sometimes deliberately imported for this purpose. Elsewhere, however, muskrats are a pest because their tunnelling breaches banks and dykes. In Europe muskrats are raised on ranches for their fur but many escape and go wild. They

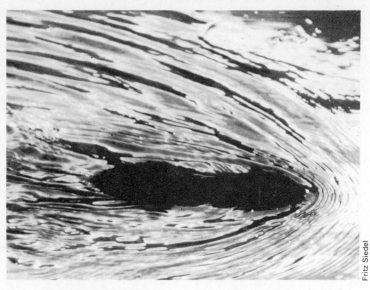

Fritz Siedel

◁ *Bankside contentment, the muskrat* **Ondatra zibethicus** *sits happily in the shallow water. This large vole has a coat of long coarse guard hairs and a short dense layer of soft hairs. This underfur is sold as musquash.*
▷ *At home in the water, the muskrat is well adapted for swimming. The hindfeet are partially webbed and the tail flattened and used as a rudder.*
▽ *Water home, a muskrat builds a winter retreat.*

may cause serious damage as there are few large marshes where they can live without coming into conflict with man. They are a severe pest in Holland and were only just prevented from becoming established in Britain. Their rapid rate of breeding and the absence of natural enemies in Europe allowed them to spread rapidly. In 1927 five females and four males escaped from a farm in Scotland. Three years later nearly 900 of their descendants had been trapped. One point in their favour though is that

they are very tasty, and are marketed in the United States as 'marsh rabbit' or 'Chesapeake terrapin'.

| class | **Mammalia** |
|---|---|
| order | **Rodentia** |
| family | **Cricetidae** |
| genus & species | ***Ondatra obscura*** *O. zibethica Newfoundland muskrat* |

Lynwood M Chace

# Mussel

*Various kinds of bivalve molluscs are known as mussels, including horse mussel* **Modiolus modiolus**, *fan mussel* **Pinna fragilis** *and the freshwater swan mussels* **Anodonta spp.** *The best known, however, is the common or edible mussel* **Mytilus edulis**, *a species widely distributed over most of the temperate and subtropical coasts of the northern hemisphere, where it is found in very large numbers on the shores and down to about 30 ft. There are closely related species in other parts of the world. Both 'mussel' and 'muscle' derive from Latin* **musculus**, *a small mouse.*

*The adult edible mussel is 2—5 in. long but may be much smaller in some localities or, exceptionally, nearly 9 in. Typically blue or purple, or sometimes brown or with radial dark brown or purple markings, each of the two valves making up the shell is broad at the hind end and narrow at the front. Near the front end is the hinge and the elastic ligament that pushes the shell open when the muscles inside relax. There is one of these 'adductor' muscles at each end, running from one valve to the other, that at the hind end being largest and strongest. Their points of attachment can be seen as 'scars' inside empty shells, together with those of other muscles that withdraw the foot. When the mussel is submerged, this long brownish foot may be seen protruding from between the valves. Not only is it used for moving about, but also for making the tough protein threads, forming the byssus or beard, with which the mussel is normally anchored.*

△ *A series of attachments. Mussels, themselves now covered by small organisms, coat the mooring chain of a ship in the Mediterranean.*

▽ *Empty mussel shells form the remains of some starfishes' meals. Starfish and man are probably the worst enemies of mussels.*

G Mundey

## Millions of mussels

Secured by their byssus threads as by guy ropes, edible musssels are found from high on the shore to a depth of a few fathoms, principally near low tide mark, on rocks, pier piles or stones lying in mud or gravel. Few molluscs can rival them in abundance. Exceptionally, concentrations of 16 000 to a square foot have been seen and in some parts of the coast there may be 20 million in a mile stretch. In the northern hemisphere they range from the Kara Sea to the Mediterranean, on both coasts of North America and around Japan, as well as in a few other localities outside these areas, but not in the high arctic. The other species, such as the California mussel, *M. californianus* and the Australian mussel, *M. obscurus*, are so like the common mussel of the northern hemisphere that only an expert can tell them apart. Mussels can live in sea water considerably diluted with fresh water and can tolerate even further dilution for a while by clamping their shells. The adults rarely move about but the young do so fairly often, sometimes freely by means of their long extensible foot and sometimes by throwing out fresh byssus threads to pull themselves along with and then cutting loose the old byssus threads.

Fritz Siedel

## Water purifiers

Mussels feed by straining fine particles from the water together with small floating organisms like diatoms. On each side of the foot is a large gill, each double so there are actually four similar 'gill plates'. Each bears countless cilia beating in such a way as to draw water in at the hind end of the body, through the gill plates and out through a special opening at the rear. The inhalant and exhalant currents do not pass through siphons as well-developed as those of the cockle (p 470). As the food particles hit the gills they are caught up in mucus given out by the gills and are driven with it by cilia to the edges. Here the mucus enters special ciliated channels and moves forwards towards the mouth. On either side of the mouth are two much smaller gill-like flaps that sort the particles, directing the indigestible matter out along special rejection paths and the digestible into the mouth. All this requires the coordinated action of several different kinds of cilia with different functions. Some indication of what happens may be obtained by opening a mussel (cutting the adductor muscles), scattering powder on the gills and watching how it is carried along by the cilia.

Mussels and other animals feeding on microscopic particles are ultimate scavengers in the sea. Some idea of the effect they have can be gauged from an incident that took place at the Millport Marine Biological Station, in Scotland. There was a tank containing a number of common mussels and although there were other animals in it the mussels kept the water so clean that anyone looking down on it from above was unaware that there was any water in the tank. One day a visitor to the Station leaned over this tank and to get a closer look at the animals on the bottom of it, he lowered his face — right into the water!

## Only one month's freedom

The breeding season varies with the locality, and also with the temperature of the water. Each egg is only about $\frac{1}{300}$ in. across but a single female may release 5−12 or even 25 million of them. The eggs are grouped together in short pink rods when they are shed, but these break up on sinking to the bottom. They are fertilised by sperm also released into the water and give rise to free-swimming ciliated embryos after about 5 hours. Towards the end of the second day, the shell appears, at first horn yellow and without a hinge. At this stage, the larvae feed and propel themselves by means of ciliated lobes projecting from their shells. Later the young mussels lose these lobes and improve their buoyancy by giving out a bubble of gas between their valves. Later, this is released, the larvae sink to the bottom, settle and give up their floating life. The free larval stage lasts about a month and by the time of settling, the larvae measure about $\frac{1}{50}$ − $\frac{1}{25}$ in. Having settled, the young mussels may glide about rapidly on their ciliated feet or they may simply anchor themselves with the byssus threads. Until they are about $\frac{1}{8}$ in. long, they have the choice to do either of these, and they sometimes do them even at the surface of the sea, presumably held there by surface tension.

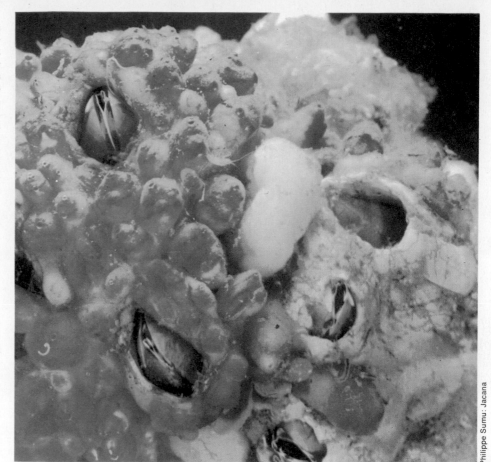

Philippe Sumu: Jacana

△ *Peaceful co-existence. Mussels* **Mytilus edulis***, barnacles and a colony of tunicates grow side by side but independently.*

▽ *Permanent fixtures. Once anchored, adult mussels rarely move about although the young often do so for short periods.*

DB Lewis

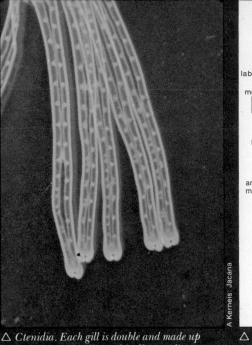

△ *Ctenidia. Each gill is double and made up of two rows of ctenidia used in filter feeding.*

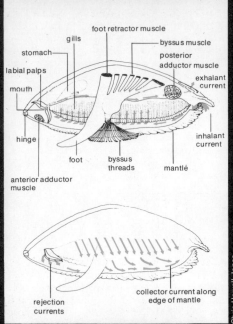

foot retractor muscle
gills
byssus muscle
stomach
posterior
adductor muscle
labial palps
exhalant
current
mouth
hinge
inhalant
current
foot
byssus
threads
mantle
anterior adductor
muscle
rejection
currents
collector current along
edge of mantle

△ *Ciliary currents of **Mytilus**. Top: food currents. Bottom: rejection currents.*

△ *When a mussel is opened the orange gills and shell muscles can be seen quite clearly.*

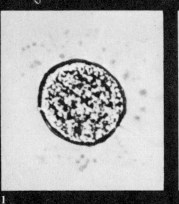

**1**

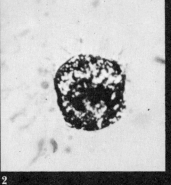

**2**

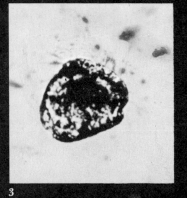

**3**

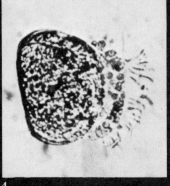

**4**

*Developmental stages of **Mytilus edulis**. Numbers 1 − 4 about 300 × lifesize. Numbers 5 − 7 about 70 × lifesize. Within 12 hours after fertilisation a ciliated trochophore (1) is formed. A later stage (2) shows some long cilia concentrated at one end. A small flat shell forms, young veliger (3).*

*This finally encompasses the whole animal now called a straight-hinge veliger (4). The long cilia form a velum used by the 3 day old larva for swimming. A 2nd larval shell is secreted, veliconcha (5). This is the main larval stage and lasts 20 days. All the stages from 1 − 5 are planktonic.*

*A foot grows, pediveliger (6), and the larva stops being planktonic and goes to the sea bottom seeking a place of attachment to change into the adult form. This stage lasts 4 − 5 days. The larva attaches with byssus thread and changes into young adult, the early plantigrade (7).*

**5**

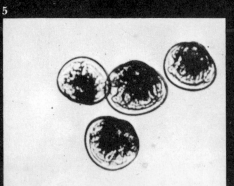

**6**

**7**

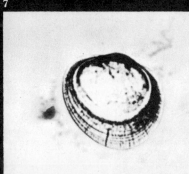

### The world is against them

Mussels have many enemies, including dog whelks, herring gulls, oystercatchers, ducks and walruses as well as fish such as flounders and plaice. Starfish are often their chief predator, however, apart from man. Mussels are considered large enough to eat when just over 2 in. long and two or more years old. They are generally collected by dredging or raking, but in France they are farmed by a method said to have been invented in 1235 by a shipwrecked Irishman whose original intention was to construct a trap for sea birds. In this, tall hurdles are planted in the mud on the foreshore and on these the mussels are hung in bags of netting which eventually rot away after the molluscs have fastened themselves to the hurdles. For commercial purposes mussels are carefully washed and care must be taken by anyone collecting mussels for themselves, since their method of feeding is ideal for concentrating the bacteria in sewage, including those of typhoid. Sometimes, too, mussels produce an alkaloid that can cause death by stopping the breathing. They do,

however, sometimes have small pearls inside them but these are no longer valued! As well as being sold as food, mussels are useful as bait in long-line fishing, as fertilisers, as chicken feed and sometimes for stabilizing the foreshore. At St Anne's-on-Sea, in Lancashire, mussels settle every 2 years on a gravel bed. During the next 2 years they form a mass of mussels and mud 2 ft deep. Then heavy seas roll the whole mass up like a carpet and smash it to pieces, after which the gravel is repopulated with mussels and the process starts all over again. Even so, the mussel carpet protects the foreshore from violent erosion.

## Cloth of gold

The byssus threads are so strong that they can be woven into cloth. There are in various museums objects made from the beards of common fan mussels, for example gloves. The cloth woven from the larger bivalves was extensively used centuries ago to make these garments that had a golden sheen, and were used by the aristocracy especially those

of southern Europe. The Field of the Cloth of Gold was an historic meeting between Henry VIII and the King of France. It was so called because so many of the nobles assembled there wore tunics made from the beards of bivalves. It had nothing to do with gold thread. Some other bivalves themselves make unusual use of their own beards. One *Modiolaria* lives embedded in a nest of its own byssus threads. The file shell *Lima* a relative of the scallop, builds a similar nest up to 10 in. across by darning bits of sea-bed debris together. Such a nest may contain an adult as well as several young, so there is a superficial similarity with a bird's nest.

| | |
|---|---|
| phylum | **Mollusca** |
| class | **Bivalvia** |
| sub-class | **Lamellibranchia** |
| order | **Filibranchia** |
| family | **Mytilidae** |
| genus & species | *Mytilus edulis* |

▽ *A strong attachment. A mussel* **Mytilus edulis** *clings to the rock by its byssus threads.* ▽ *Fan mussel byssus gathered for spinning.*

▽ *Hand made. These gloves have been woven from the tough byssus threads of many mussels. In the past much cloth was also woven.*

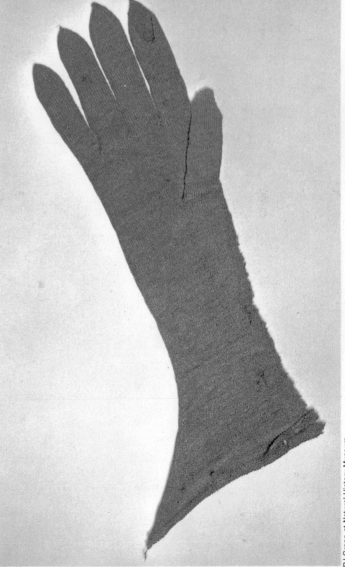

Heather Angel

PJ Green at Natural History Museum

PJ Green at Natural History Museum

# Mynah

Mynahs—often called mynah birds—are large starlings living in southern Asia. The largest, measuring 15 in. long, is the Indian hill mynah, sometimes called the greater hill mynah, popular today in many parts of the world as a talking cage bird. Often referred to in India as a grackle, it is a glossy black with yellow wattles. The common mynah, sometimes called the Indian mynah, is 10 in. long, and is brown and black with white wing patches. It has a short crest and patches of orange coloured skin around the eyes. In both, the orange yellow beak is thick, curved and shorter than the head. The short crown feathers curve inwards making a parting down the middle of the head. The tail is short, nearly square at the end, and the wings are blunt. The strong legs and feet are yellowish. The bank mynah, or Bengal mynah has buff instead of white on the wings. In all species, the male and female are much alike, the male usually differing in having slightly more extensive wattles and slightly brighter coloured legs and feet than the female.

The hill mynah ranges from India and Ceylon to the Greater Sunda Islands of Indonesia. The common mynah is found in India, especially southern India, and Ceylon. The Chinese crested mynah lives further north, in southern China, from the Yangtse to Yunnan, and also in Burma. It is similar to the hill mynah but without wattles and has a small ragged tuft of feathers—the crest—above the base of the bill. Farther east are the 3 species of Papuan mynahs of New Guinea, and there are other species on the islands of the southwest Pacific. Related to the Papuan mynahs is the golden-crested mynah of Burma, Laos, Vietnam and Malaya, 8½ in. long, glossy black with yellow on the head. There is a broad yellow patch on the wing, and a long yellow crest lying flat on the head. The bill, legs and feet are orange.

The Indian hill mynah is divided into a number of subspecies based mainly on differences in size and in the development of the wattles. In some subspecies these are ragged flaps of yellow to orange skin, in others, merely patches of naked skin.

## Quarrelsome birds

The hill mynahs travel through forests in small noisy flocks uttering their low hoarse chuckles and loud ringing whistles. Besides being noisy they seem to be quarrelsome. The common mynah is more like the European starling in habits, being a bird of the open country, and mainly a ground feeder. It lives in flocks, is noisy and quarrelsome and is given to what has been called foot-wrestling. This begins with a good deal of leaping about, wing flapping and low cries, followed by wrestling with the feet on the ground. Other mynahs vary slightly between foraging through the trees, as in the hill mynah, and ground foraging. In all the food is fruit and insects, sometimes small carrion, the proportions of plant and animal food varying with the season and other circumstances. Like the European starlings, they roost communally, and in large numbers in the case of the common mynah.

## Decorated nests

The nest is usually in a hole in a tree but it may be in the open when it takes the form of a globular nest with a side entrance, or it may be in a hole in a bank. The bank mynah always builds in holes in vertical banks. The materials used include twigs, grass and dead leaves but almost any small material such as feathers, paper, rags, beetle wing cases even a sloughed snake skin may be used. A tendency has been noticed for mynahs to use coloured materials for the nest, especially the petals of large highly coloured flowers. Clutches vary from 2—9 eggs with 3—5 being the more usual number. The eggs are usually bluish-green with brown blotches. Incubation, by the hen only, lasts about 14 days, and both parents feed the babies which are hatched pink and naked. Quills start to grow at about 11 days. Their eyes open at 6 days.

△ A glint in the eye of the hill mynah, a glossy black bird with a thick, bright orange beak.
▽ Noisy, quarrelsome starlings of Asia, common mynahs are ground feeders and birds of open country.

Jane Burton: Photo Res

Russ Kinne: Photo Res

## Globe trotters

The outstanding feature of mynahs, as with starlings generally, is their ability to mimic sounds, including the calls of other birds, as well as human speech. This, together with their attractive appearance, has led to some species being exported in large numbers. In many parts of the world they have become established in the wild and in some countries are becoming a pest. The common mynah has been introduced into South Africa, Australia, New Zealand, the Solomon Islands, Hawaii, Fiji, Mauritius and many other islands in the Pacific, Indian and South Atlantic oceans.

## Mynah problems

On Mauritius they have been beneficial because of the insects they eat, including the cane-borer, a pest of sugar plantations. It is said that the mynahs now in Natal, South Africa, and spreading across to the Transvaal were introduced in 1888. Margaret Cuthbertson, in *African Wild Life* for March 1952, quotes an obituary notice which mentions that Mr Leon St Guillaume released three pairs of mynahs brought from Mauritius from the top of a double-decker horse tram in 1888. Today it is impossible to assess accurately the numbers of mynahs in Durban. They haunt gardens, parks and beaches and roost noisily in trees.

Rothschild's mynah, Rothschild's starling or Rothschild's grackle, as it is variously known, is native to the tiny island of Bali in Indonesia. Here, as in all countries where mynahs are native, they are kept as cage birds but the destruction of the forests on Bali, a heavily populated island, has led to a situation in which there are probably more of this species in captivity than in the wild and fears are expressed for its survival. Vancouver Island in British Columbia, also has its mynah problem. Crested mynahs from southeast Asia were introduced there at the turn of the century, about the same time as common mynahs were getting established in Natal. The crested mynahs flourished, reached a population of about 20 000 and then levelled off at this figure. Why the population has remained stationary is a puzzle, but is a welcome situation because if the mynahs should spread south they would be near the fruit farms of California—and another pest would be present in the orchards.

| class | **Aves** |
|---|---|
| order | **Passeriformes** |
| family | **Sturnidae** |
| genera & species | **Acridotheres cristatellus** *Chinese crested mynah* |
| | **A. ginginianus** *bank mynah* |
| | **A. tristis** *common mynah* |
| | **Gracula religiosa** *hill mynah* |
| | **Leucospar rothschildi** *Rothschild's mynah* |
| | **Mino coronatus** *golden-crested mynah* |
| | **M. dumontii** *Papuan mynah* |

Russ Kinne: Photo Res

△ *Rothschild's mynah, commonly kept as a cage bird, is native to the island of Bali in Indonesia.*
▽ *Common mynah, first introduced into South Africa in 1888, goes for a ride on a Burchell's zebra.*

Jane Burton: Photo Res

# Narwhal

The narwhal, the 'unicorn' of the whale family, is related to the beluga (p 190). Its peculiar feature is the single twisted horn on the forehead which formed the basis of the mythical unicorn. This horn is usually found only on males. The adults of both sexes have a single pair of teeth in the upper jaw. In the male one tooth grows out through the upper lip to form a tusk 8—9 ft long. Because of the great development of the single tooth, which nearly always has a left-handed twist, the skull, itself, is lopsided. Very rarely both teeth develop into tusks and occasionally females with tusks are found.

Narwhals reach lengths of 13—16 ft, excluding the tusk. The head is rounded and the dorsal fin is no more than a ridge 1—2 in. high and extending 2—3 ft along the back. The flippers are small and rounded. Adult narwhals are greyish white with blackish spots on the back. Young narwhals are generally darker and very old individuals may be almost white in colour.

It is rare for narwhals to be found outside the Arctic Sea. They have been seen only a short way from the North Pole and the southern limit of their range is generally around 70° North, about the level of the North Cape of Norway and Point Barrow, Alaska. Narwhals occasionally stray farther south and have been stranded on the coasts of Britain and Holland.

## Caught in icy traps

Narwhals are quite common and have survived the general slaughter of whales because of the inaccessibility of their Arctic home. They usually live in small parties, or pods of up to 50, but these sometimes combine to form huge herds of several thousand animals. The herds may be mixed or segregated by sexes. Narwhals can swim quite rapidly and when they surface their breath is exhaled with a shrill whistle, after which the narwhals lie motionless at the surface for a few minutes before diving.

In the summer narwhals move into bays and sometimes ascend rivers, one having been found 700 miles up the Yukon River. Occasionally narwhals get trapped in the bays by ice which gradually covers the whole bay. The narwhals attempt to keep breathing holes open and when forced together at one small pool provide the Eskimos with a chance to lay in a whole winter's supply of meat and blubber, for a 'savssat', as the Eskimos call it, may contain 1 000 narwhals.

Narwhals feed mainly on cuttlefish, together with squid and crustaceans. They

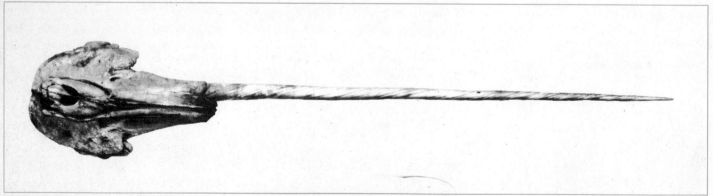

△ The few teeth of the young narwhal are lost in the adults except the left upper canine which is retained by the males and grows into a long tusk.
▽ Very rarely both upper canines grow into long straight twisted tusks, but when there are two present, they both have the same left-handed thread.

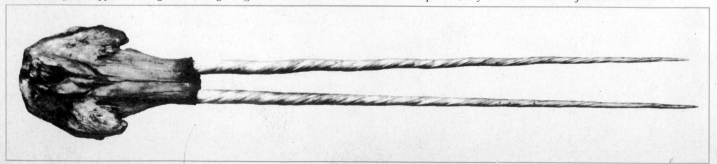

*Unicorn of the sea — the narwhal, a peculiar looking mammal, is a fast swimmer and deep diver.*

have no functional teeth and prey is grasped in the hard edges of the powerful jaws and swallowed whole.

### One or two calves

In common with many other whales very little is known of the breeding habits of narwhals; information on this is only being slowly gained as whales are kept in oceanaria. Narwhals bear one or two young, each measuring about 5 ft at birth. It has been said that the tail of the baby whale emerges from the mother's body 4–6 weeks before birth so that it can practise swimming. Although this is a Greenlander story it has been repeated in textbooks but narwhals will have to be bred in captivity to test its truth.

### Eskimo oranges

Narwhals are killed by killer whales and there is a record of a walrus disembowelling a narwhal. Eskimos and other people living around the Arctic Sea catch narwhals by harpoon or net for their meat, blubber, hide and tusks. The hide, known as muktuk, is prized for thongs because it remains supple when wet or frozen and is eaten raw as a source of Vitamin C, which is in short supply in the rest of the Eskimo's diet.

## The fabulous tusk

There have been many ingenious ideas as to the use of the narwhal's tusk. It has been supposed to be a weapon, for attacking other narwhals, or even boats, for making breathing holes in ice or for spearing food. The last two ideas can be ruled out because if tusks were necessary for such tasks one would expect females to carry them. The tusk is unlikely to be a weapon because narwhals are not aggressive. There is still no real answer to the question but it seems likely that they are an ornament for the adornment of the males, like the antlers of a deer or the wattles of a domestic cockerel.

Narwhal tusks were first brought into Europe by the Vikings or sent south by Siberians. They were prized as ivory and for a magical ability to neutralise poisons. In the Middle Ages a narwhal tusk cup was a good investment for anyone with too many enemies. Not surprisingly the beautiful, twisted horn became linked with the legendary unicorn. Presumably the story was fostered by traders who knew the origin of the tusks and only in the mid-17th century was the famous 'unicorn horn' reidentified as belonging to the narwhal.

| class | **Mammalia** |
|---|---|
| order | **Cetacea** |
| family | **Delphinidae** |
| genus & species | *Monodon monoceros* |

▽ *Hunted down for their food content, their hide and their highly prized tusks, dead narwhals are dragged onto the beach before being carved up.*

# Natterjack

The most distinctive feature of the natterjack toad is a yellow line running down the head and back from the snout to the vent. This has given rise to one of the local names of 'goldenback'. It is very similar to the common toad in appearance but rather smaller, the maximum length being just over 3 in. There is no marked difference in size between the sexes. The legs are proportionately shorter than those of the common toad. The body is greyish or pale yellowish-brown, sometimes with distinct spots of brown, reddish, yellow or green. The underside is yellowish-white with dark spots, and the legs are barred with black. The skin of the upperparts is covered with wart-like glands as in the common toad but the two large parotid glands behind the eyes are smaller than in the common toad. The male can be distinguished by its stronger forelimbs and, during the breeding season, by the blackish patches of horny skin on the hands, the so-called nuptial pads, and a bluish patch of skin on the throat. The green toad **Bufo viridis** which is very closely related to the natterjack, lives in Europe. It lacks the stripe running down the back except in the parts of its range where the natterjack is absent.

Natterjacks are confined to Europe, being common in France and Spain, but ranging from southern Sweden in the north to the Gulf of Riga and Poland in the east. In the British Isles they are restricted to certain localities in England and Scotland, and to Co. Kerry in Ireland.

John Markham

△ *That expansive feeling? An extremely fat female natterjack spreads herself on a rock while a younger one crawls around her. Secretions from the mucous glands prevent the sun drying the skin out.*

▽ *A squatter by nature. A natterjack toad sits squarely on its short plump legs, which are so short that it cannot jump like other toads, but runs instead, sometimes quite fast.*

## Seaside toad

Because of their short hind legs natterjacks do not jump but move at a fast run, and in some parts they are called the running toad. They run down their prey which consists of small animals, such as spiders, insects, worms and snails.

Natterjacks are nearly always found in sandy places where they can burrow easily, such as in the sand dunes along the coast, but because of the increasing development of seaside areas, natterjacks are becoming scarce. In England, their last strongholds are the counties of Dorset, Hampshire, Surrey and Lancashire. It is difficult to ascertain the exact distribution of natterjacks because they will suddenly appear in an area where they have never been seen before, then disappear, moving to a new breeding ground.

In loose sand a natterjack can dig itself out of sight within a few seconds, using its hindlegs to push itself in. In firmer soil it scrapes a hole with its forelegs, shooting the loosened soil back under its belly. Deserted burrows of other animals may be used by a group of natterjacks. In the winter natterjacks hibernate in burrows 1 ft or more deep and have been known to climb walls of sand, wintering in sand martin burrows.

Natterjacks usually emerge at night but they are sometimes active during the day when they may be seen sunning themselves. Their skin is not as dry as that of common toads, being kept moist by secretions from mucous glands, which allows them to come out in quite strong daylight.

P Morris

### Breeding in salt water

The breeding season is lengthy and in exceptional years it may start in late March and continue to August. Natterjacks are not good swimmers and during breeding they are usually found among reeds, not far from the banks of the breeding pools. They are able to breed in brackish pools near the sea because both eggs and tadpoles can survive quite strong salt concentrations. They also breed in ditches and puddles devoid of water plants. Mating usually takes place at night, the males attracting females with a loud croak of *ra, ra, ra* that, in chorus, can be heard for a mile or more. The vocal sac under the chin is three times the size of the head when it is extended and the forelegs have to be straightened to allow it to expand. The eggs are laid in a few hours. The strings are shorter than those of the common toad, measuring 5–6 ft long and containing up to 4 000 eggs. When first laid, the eggs, each $\frac{1}{13}$ in. in diameter, lie in two rows within the jelly string, but as they grow they push each other aside to form a single row. The tadpoles emerge within 5–10 days of the eggs being laid. They are the smallest tadpoles of any European amphibian, rarely more than an inch long, and greyish black with bronzy spots. The young toads, which measure only $\frac{1}{3}$ in. after the tail has been lost, leave the water 5–8 weeks after hatching. By autumn they are twice as large but they do not become fully grown until 4–5 years old.

### Nasty smells

When alarmed a natterjack blows itself up in the same way as a common toad. It is also said to 'feign death' by spreading itself flat on the ground. When handled, natterjacks exude a white liquid from the skin which has been described as smelling like burnt gunpowder or boiling rubber.

## Change of life

Natterjacks are mainly land animals, living on dry sandy soil and only taking to water for the few hours necessary for mating and egg-laying. It has been found, however, that they can be trained to take up an aquatic way of life. They can be conditioned to gradually spending more and more time in water until they are living permanently in water. So profound is the conditioning that if a trained natterjack is liberated it voluntarily continues its aquatic life. Furthermore, such toads change their basic behaviour patterns and perform frog-like actions that they never use normally. The implication of such experiments are that the behaviour of amphibians cannot be assumed to be rigid and that they are capable of learning or adapting their habits.

| class | **Amphibia** |
|-------|-------------|
| order | **Salientia** |
| family | **Bufonidae** |
| genus & species | *Bufo calamita* |

△ *Dead or alive? Two natterjacks pose together as dead wood.*

▽ *Split level toad. Natterjacks are not good swimmers by nature although they can be trained.*

# Nautilus

The nautilus lives in a spiral shell which is
one of the most beautiful of all shells,
once the outside has been cleaned. It is
ivory-coloured on the outside, marked with
a zebra pattern in reddish-brown. Inside
it is lined with mother-of-pearl. The shell
is never more than 1 ft across and inside
it is divided into about 30 chambers in a
well-grown nautilus, the animal itself
living in the outermost chamber. When it
swims this newest chamber is lowermost.

It is sometimes spoken of as the pearly
nautilus to distinguish it from the paper
nautilus or argonaut (see p 82).

**Nautilus pompilius**—*patterned shell
(about lifesize).*

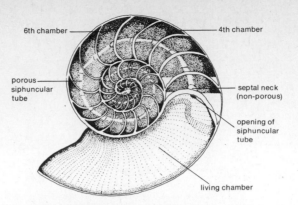

6th chamber — 4th chamber

porous siphuncular tube

septal neck (non-porous)

opening of siphuncular tube

living chamber

*Section of a* **Nautilus macromphalus**.
*White areas represent typical levels of
liquid within the 30 chambers of the shell.*

**Nautilus pompilius**—*sectioned shell.*

PJ Green at Natural History Museum

In spite of having similar names, the two are only distantly related since they belong to separate orders. The main distinction is that the nautilus has four gills against the two gills of the argonaut, but there are other basic differences.

The six species of nautilus live in the southwest Pacific although in geological times they were widespread throughout the world. They are living fossils, the only survivors of an order that has almost completely died out.

## Delayed knowledge

Although the shell of the nautilus has been known since the end of the 16th century, the animal itself was not properly studied until 1831, when a Mr Bennett brought one, preserved in spirits, from the New Hebrides, in the South Pacific, to Mr Richard Owen, at the Royal College of Surgeons in London. Over a hundred years elapsed before the living animal was studied. In 1962 Dr Anna Bidder, of Cambridge University, went to New Caledonia where for 2 months she watched 40 nautilus in aquaria. Four years later, Dr EJ Denton of the Plymouth Laboratory and Dr JB Gilpin-Brown of the University of Auckland, New Zealand, made further studies in the Loyalty Islands. Until then most of our information about how the animal lives had been from dead or dying animals, or based on the tales of local fishermen. Much of this information has now been found to be incorrect.

## Swimming by jet propulsion

The nautilus does not creep over the bottom with its tentacles as was once thought but it swims, mainly at night, driving itself along by a form of jet propulsion. The funnel in an octopus or cuttlefish is not muscular but water is drawn in and driven out through it by movements in the whole mantle. In nautilus the funnel is strongly muscular and the mantle lacks any strong muscle. so it is the funnel which pumps the water. This is in two halves. When the halves are separate the water is taken in, and when they come together, their edges overlapping, the muscles in them contract and water is squirted out. The gills are inside the funnel, so breathing takes place at the same time. Also, in an octopus, squid or cuttlefish, there is an ink-sac within the mantle cavity and ink can be squirted through the funnel by contractions of the mantle itself. A nautilus would not be able to move its mantle in this way, and it has no ink-sac.

During the day the nautilus remains near the bottom, either clinging by its tentacles to a solid support or suspended just off the bottom and mostly withdrawn into its shell with the eye just clear of the optic notch. It withdraws completely when alarmed. While suspended in water it shows no movement except for the pulsation in the funnel, or a slight rocking movement of the whole shell. It is said to be able to swim fast but this has yet to be confirmed.

## Holding without suckers

There are many tentacles which are divided into three groups. There is one in front of, and one behind, each eye, then an outer ring of 19 pairs and an inner circle of numerous

△ *Ancestral relative, 200 million year old fossil ammonite shell (2 × natural size).*

Natural History Museum

tentacles around the mouth and its powerful beak. The first and third of these tentacle rings can be withdrawn into their sheaths. The tentacles, unlike those of octopuses and squids, have no suckers or hooks but are ridged, giving them a grip so strong that a tentacle may be torn away from its base once it has taken hold of something solid. When searching for food some of the tentacles are extended. As soon as they grasp a fish or a crab they pass it to the tentacles around the mouth which hold it while the beak bites pieces out of it.

## Buoyed up with gases

Probably the first four chambers of the shell are formed while the young nautilus is still within the egg or using up the food in the yolk sac. After that a new chamber is probably formed every 2 or 3 weeks, the nautilus being connected with the chambers by a siphuncle—a fleshy stalk in a chalky tube. Each new chamber is laid down by the body of the nautilus and at the same time a concave partition seals off the chamber behind it. This is slowly emptied of water by the siphuncle acting as a wick, passing the water from the old chamber into the body. At the same time gases dissolved in the body fluid are given off so filling the chamber. Although the shell is so heavy relative to the body it is buoyed up by these gas-filled chambers. Because the centre of buoyancy is lower than the centre of gravity the nautilus is always body downmost, just as the basket of a balloon is always lower than the balloon itself.

# Foundations of fame

• The account given here is a much simplified version of all that is known about nautilus. Its anatomy is complicated, especially that of the tentacles, and so is its biology. The recent studies of the living animal on the spot have solved some problems but left many other questions still unanswered. It is of interest to recall how this animal led to the foundation of one man's reputation in the 19th century. A certain Mr Richard Owen, assistant-conservator of the Museum of the Royal College of Surgeons in London, and then only 19 years of age, heard that a fellow student, Mr George Bennett, was about to sail to the South Pacific. He 'earnestly charged his friend to do his utmost to obtain, and bring home in alcohol, a specimen of the much-coveted Pearly Nautilus'. On August 24, 1829, Mr Bennett saw a living nautilus on the surface, looking 'like a dead tortoiseshell cat', as one of the sailors said. It was caught with a boathook, and its shell was damaged, but its body was captured intact. This was brought back to London, where it was studied in detail by Owen, who published his results in a masterly treatise. Owen, as soon as his book was published, was about to set out for Paris to show the results of his dissections to the great Baron Cuvier, when he heard of Cuvier's death. He went on to earn for himself the reputation of the greatest anatomist of his time. He died Sir Richard Owen, loaded with honours, in 1892. Yet few people recall that of all his brilliant works, Owen climbed to fame on the carcass of a nautilus brought in spirit from the other side of the world.

| phylum | **Mollusca** |
|---|---|
| class | **Cephalopoda** |
| order | **Tetrabranchia** |
| family | **Nautilidae** |
| genus & species | *Nautilus macromphalus* *N. pompilius* *others* |

▽ *Submarine wanderer. A free swimming **Nautilus macromphalus**, buoyed up by gases in its shell, propels itself along by pumping water through its funnel, and not by creeping along the sea floor.*

Anna M Bidder

# Needlefish

*Needlefish is an alternative name for garfish, which avoids confusion with the North American gar or garpike. Garfish is Old English for spearfish. It is apt not only with reference to the shape of the fish but also to its habit of launching itself into the air. The garfish has a long slender body and its jaws are drawn out to form a beak-like snout. The total length may be 3 ft or more, and up to 4½ ft in tropical species. The mouth is armed with many sharp teeth. The back is blue-green, the belly silver. All the fins are small, the unpaired, soft-rayed fins, and the pelvics being set well back. Garfishes are noted for having green bones, hence their alternative name of greenbone.*

*Related to needlefishes are the halfbeaks and skippers and some indication of the evolution of the related flying fish can be drawn from their study. Halfbeaks are usually smaller, up to 18 in. long with a stouter body. The upper jaw is very short while the lower jaw is long, as in the garfish. Some tropical species may, however, reach 6 ft or more. Otherwise the two kinds of fish are very alike except that some of the halfbeaks live in freshwater, although most are marine.*

*The skippers, sometimes known as sauries, have only a very short beak and they have 5—7 finlets behind the dorsal fin and the same behind the anal fin.*

*There are 60 species of garfishes in tropical and temperate seas, 70 species of halfbeaks and 4 species of skippers. All three of these fishes are, however, most numerous in tropical seas.*

## Skipping and skittering

Garfish, halfbeaks and skippers often. leap in and out of the water or skitter along the surface for quite a distance. They skitter with the head and forepart of the body out of water with their submerged tail vibrating rapidly from side to side. Garfishes, which are very fast swimmers, often feed in shoals, skimming along at the surface, and frequently transfix smaller fishes with their spear-like beak. Their jaws are armed with numerous teeth, not to masticate the food, but to prevent the prey, which is swallowed whole, escaping. The stomach is straight so it can take in whole prey. Halfbeaks are even more adept at skittering and they probably do so when trying to escape from enemies, such as tunny and swordfish. It is possible that they may also skitter along when feeding as they are vegetarian, eating mainly green seaweed. Their open mouths would also take in a certain amount of planktonic crustaceans and molluscs which often float at the surface.

## Playful fishes?

Garfishes, also known as longtoms in some parts of the world, sometimes leap over the back of a turtle or a floating log, often performing somersaults. This action has all the appearance of play. The antics of halfbeaks are even more playful: one of them will swim rapidly at a floating object and, just as the tip of its long lower jaw is under the object, it flips itself over, usually to land the other side, facing in the opposite direction. Sometimes it repeats this several times.

## Evolution of flying fishes

Whether leaping and skittering are necessary for feeding, escape or merely play, it is easy to see how, if garfishes, halfbeaks and skippers had large paired fins, they could remain airborne by gliding on spread fins. This is precisely the case with their relatives, the flying fishes. This sequence is an indication of how the large pectoral fins of flying fishes (p 794) could have evolved.

## Halfbeak baby garfishes

Spawning takes place in shallow water, in spring or early summer. Garfish eggs, $\frac{1}{8}$ in. diameter, have sticky filaments which anchor them to each other and to objects such as seaweeds. They hatch in 5 weeks, in the species *Belone belone*, of the eastern Atlantic, the larvae being $\frac{1}{2}$ in. long on hatching. They are shaped like the adult except that only the lower jaw is prominent, so they look more like young halfbeaks. The lower jaw

▽ *Freshwater halfbeak, small, playful relative of the needlefish. The large fin area at the hind end drives this torpedo-shaped fish.*

Barry Pengilley

Photo Aquatics

△ *Netted skipper* **Scomberesox**. *Skippers are 12—14 in. long at the most and can be distinguished from the rest of the family by their short jaws. They got their name from the way in which they skitter over the surface of the water with their submerged tail vibrating rapidly from side to side.*

continues to grow longer, while the upper jaw remains short until the young garfish are just over 2 in. long, when the upper jaw begins to elongate. At the end of the first summer the young fishes, moving in shoals, go farther out to sea, and this annual migration continues throughout their lifetime with great regularity. Off the coasts of Europe this brings them inshore with the mackerel, on which they feed, and into contact with the herring shoals.

Halfbeaks lay eggs similar to those of the garfish and development follows much the same lines except for some of the freshwater halfbeaks of the Indo-Australian region which bear live young. Some young halfbeaks look like floating seaweed. They react to danger by going stiff and floating passively so they look like dead pieces of seaweed.

## Tragic encounter

That the fish should have been called garfish, or spearfish, from early times, may have been connected with something more than its spearlike shape or its habit of leaping from the water like a spear launched through the air. In the *Malayan Nature Journal*, May 1968, is an account of a Singapore customs vessel taking in tow a Sumatran rowing sampan with seven Indonesians on board. After a while one of the sampan's crew collapsed, bleeding profusely from the neck. He died before the boats reached the shore and an autopsy showed there was a fragment of bone in his neck. It was part of a garfish jaw, the fish having leaped out of the water, not with aggressive intent but in the normal way of garfishes, stabbed the Indonesian and fallen into the sea again. Apparently the people of Malaysia have long been aware of this danger but their ideas have hitherto been treated as folklore.

| class | **Pisces** | | |
|---|---|---|---|
| order | **Atheriniformes** | | |
| families | **Belonidae** *garfishes* | | |
| | **Exocoetidae** *halfbeaks* | | |
| | **Scomberesocidae** *skippers* | | |

▽ *Fish hooks. Many unsuspecting fish have been impaled on these teeth before being swallowed whole. Garfish, also known as longtoms, are fast swimmers and often feed in shoals. They are noted for the way in which they leap playfully over floating objects, sometimes doing somersaults over turtles' backs.*

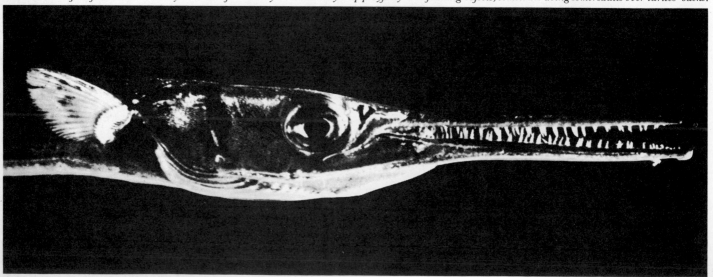

# Neopilina

*In the eyes of a non-scientist neopilina is a somewhat uninteresting animal—just another limpet. To the scientist it is one of the most exciting discoveries of the mid-20th century. Apart from the fact that it is yet another living fossil, the whole circumstances of its discovery are astonishing.*

*In 1952, when the Danish research ship **Galathea** was nearing the end of her cruise in the Pacific, her dredge was hauled up from a depth of 11 878 ft off the coast of Costa Rica. In it were 10 living limpet-like animals and 3 empty shells. They belonged to a new species, of a group of molluscs known as the Monoplacophora, which seemed to have died out 350 million years ago. Each empty shell was spoon-shaped, thin, fragile and semi-transparent, coloured pale yellowish white. The largest was 1½ in. long, 1¼ in. wide and ½ in. high. The top of the shell rose to a peak the apex of which tilted over at one end. The inside was a lustrous mother-of-pearl.*

*The body of the living neopilina was like that of an ordinary limpet at first sight. When the shell it was in was laid on its back there was the usual fleshy foot, not so large as in the common limpet and it was bluish round the edges and pink in the centre. Either side of the foot was a row of 5 gills, and the mouth was at the centre of a fleshy triangle situated at one end.*

### Which way up?

Nothing quite like neopilina had been seen before the mid-20th century, and because it had been brought up from the deep ocean bed, it was not possible to do more than speculate about neopilina's way of life. The stomach was filled with radiolaria, tiny single-celled animals with jewel-like siliceous skeletons. The floor of the ocean where it had been living was dark muddy clay. Dr Henning Lemche who examined these first specimens formed the idea that they normally rested on the clay with the foot uppermost and collected the radiolaria that drifted down onto them. Sir Maurice Yonge, the leading British marine zoologist, takes the view that it could not feed this way. He agrees the foot is smaller than one would expect to carry a limpet-like animal over the soft clay bed. But he believes it moves the 'right way up', gathers its food from the seabed as it moves along helped by the gills which act not only for breathing but for locomotion. There is a pair of fleshy tentacles just behind the mouth, and these may perhaps help in gathering food into the mouth. Yonge's view is supported by the fact that each of 4 specimens caught off the coast of Peru, in 1958, had a layer of mucus on the foot, as if neopilina laid down a track of slime on which to crawl, like a garden snail.

### Four species discovered

The importance of the discovery of neopilina lies in two things. The first is that it should have been followed so quickly by the findings of other species in other parts of the world. The second is that it vindicated forecasts made by scientists about the relationships of the mollusca to other phyla of invertebrates. Concerning the first of these it is surprising, in view of what happened later, that neopilina remained undiscovered for so long. Since about 1850, when ocean dredgings began in preparation for the epic voyage of HMS *Challenger*, there have been dozens of voyages by ocean-going research vessels, some covering small areas with intensive dredging, others covering much wider areas of the ocean but not so intensively. Nothing like this remarkable mollusc was brought to the surface in that century of searching. Yet 6 years after neopilina had been found off the coast of Costa Rica, another species was caught in 19 200 ft off the coast of Peru, and 4 years later 4 specimens of a third species, each ⅔ in. long, were brought up from 8 250 ft off the coast of California. Then, in 1967, only 9 years later, a single specimen of a fourth species was caught in the Gulf of Aden in 9 000 – 11 850 ft. From these figures it seems a fair assumption that these animals have a much wider distribution than is represented by these finds.

## Missing link found

It has long been supposed that the ancestors of molluscs must have been some kind of ringed worm, like the marine bristleworms such as the fanworms (p 738). Yet if we put the two side by side they look very different. Moreover, when we look at their anatomy we find two very marked differences. A worm has a segmented body. It is also bilaterally symmetrical. That is, if we cut a worm through the middle lengthwise, the right hand half will be the mirror image of the left hand half. By contrast, a mollusc is not segmented and its body is not bilaterally symmetrical or only slightly so. Instead, it has become twisted, and this is especially true of its internal organs. So altogether molluscs and ringed worms seem to be very different kinds of animals and yet there are some things about them that suggest they must be related. Scientists studying this took the view that if ringed worms and molluscs had a common ancestor, then somewhere along the line there must have been a mollusc with a bilaterally symmetrical body, gills in pairs and a shell like a limpet. They made drawings of what this 'missing link' mollusc ought to look like. When neopilina was found it turned out to be almost identical with these drawings.

| phylum | **Mollusca** |
|---|---|
| class | **Monoplacophora** |
| order | **Tryblidiacea** |
| family | **Neopilinidae** |
| genus & species | *Neopilina adenensis* *N. ewingi* *N. galathea* *N. valeronis* |

*Neopilina galathea. The top of the shell rises to a peak which tilts over.*

*Diagram of underside of **Neopilina galathea** shows the five pairs of gills, mouth and anus.*

*On its back—the fleshy foot of **Neopilina galathea** is smaller than the common limpet's.*

foot

mouth

gill

anus

shell

Henning Lemche

Chris Howell-Jones

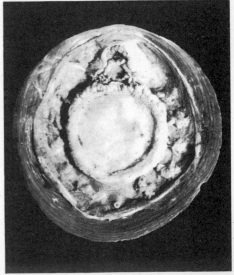

Henning Lender

# Newt

*Newts are amphibians of the salamander family. They have a life history very similar to that of frogs and toads in that the adults spend most of their life on land but return to water to breed. They are different in form, however, having long, slender bodies like those of lizards with a tail that is flattened laterally. The name comes from the Anglo-Saxon* **evete** *which became* **ewt** *and finally a newt from the transcription of the 'n' in an* **ewt**. *In Britain newt refers solely to the genus* **Triturus** *but in North America it has been applied to related animals which are sometimes, confusingly, called salamanders.*

*Newts of the genus* **Triturus** *are found in Europe, Asia, North Africa and North America. There are three species native to Britain. The most common is the smooth newt which is found all over Europe and is the only newt found in Ireland. The maximum length of smooth newts is 4 in. The colour of the body varies, but is mainly olive-brown with darker spots on the upper side and streaks on the head. The vermilion or orange underside has round black spots and the throat is yellow or white. The female is generally paler on the underside than the male and sometimes is unspotted. In the breeding season the male develops a wavy crest running along the back and tail. The palmate newt is very similar to the smooth newt, but about 1 in. shorter and with a square-sided body. In the breeding season the males of the two species can be told apart because black webs link the toes of the hindfeet of the palmate newts, and its crest is not wavy. In addition, the tail ends abruptly and a short thread, about $\frac{1}{8} - \frac{1}{4}$ in. long protrudes from the tip. The largest European newt is the crested or warty newt. It grows up to 6 in. long. The dark grey skin of the upperparts is covered with warts, while the underparts are yellow or orange and spotted with black. The distinguishing feature apart from its size is the crest of the male. From the head to the hips runs a tall, 'toothed' frill — its crest, which becomes the tail fin.*

## Hibernating on land

When they come out of hibernation in spring, newts make their way to ponds and other stretches of still water where water plants grow. They swim by lashing with their tails, but they spend much of their time resting on the mud or among the stems of plants. They can breathe through their skins but every now and then they rise to the surface to gulp air. Adult newts do not leave the water immediately breeding has finished but remain aquatic until July or August. When they come on land the crest is reabsorbed and the skin becomes rougher. The crested newt keeps its skin moist from the numerous mucus glands scattered over the surface of its body. A few individuals stay in the water all the year round, retaining their smooth skins and crests.

Hibernation begins in the autumn, when the newts crawl into crevices in the ground or under logs and stones. They cannot burrow but are very adept at squeezing themselves into cracks. Occasionally several will gather together in one place and hibernate in a tight mass.

## Gin trap teeth

The jaws of newts are lined with tiny teeth and there are two rows of teeth on the roof of the mouth. These are not used for cutting food or for chewing but merely to hold slippery, often wriggling, prey. They feed on a variety of small animals such as worms, snails and insects when on land, and crustaceans, tadpoles and insect larvae while living in water. Unlike frogs and toads, newts do not use their hands to push the food into their mouths, but gulp it down with convulsive swallows. Snails are swallowed whole, caddis flies are eaten in their cases and crested newts eat smooth newts.

## Internal fertilisation

The mating habits of newts are quite different from those of common frogs and common toads. Fertilisation is internal and is effected in a most unusual way. The male stimulates the female into breeding condition by nudging her with his snout and lashing the water with his tail. He positions himself in front of or beside her, bends his tail double and vibrates it rapidly, setting up vibrations in the water. The female is also stimulated by secretions from glands in the male's skin. At the end of the courtship the male emits a spermatophore, a mass of spermatozoa embedded in a gelatinous substance. The spermatophore sinks to the bottom and the female newt positions herself over it, then picks it up with her cloaca by pressing her body onto it.

◁▽ *A meeting on the rocks. A male crested newt gently nudges a female to stimulate her into breeding condition.*
▽ *Segmenting embryo of a crested newt.*
▷▽ *A water babe. The legless tadpole of the crested newt swimming with its large fins.*

After fertilisation the 200—300 eggs are usually laid singly on the leaves of water plants, although some American newts lay their eggs in spherical clusters. The female newt tests the leaves by smell and touch. When she has chosen a suitable one she holds it with her hindfeet, then folds the leaf over to form a tube and lays an egg in it. The jelly surrounding the egg glues the leaf firmly in place to protect it.

The eggs hatch in about 3 weeks and a more streamlined tadpole than that of a frog or toad, emerges. It is not very different from the adult newt except that it has a frill of gills and no legs. Development takes longer than in frog tadpoles but the young newts are ready to emerge by the end of summer. A few spend the winter as tadpoles, remaining in the pond until spring, even surviving being frozen into the ice.

## Nasty newts

Newts have many enemies: the young are eaten by aquatic insects and the adults by fishes, water birds, weasels, rats, hedgehogs and many other animals. The crested newt has an unpleasant secretion that is produced in the glands on the back and tail and is exuded when they are squeezed. Grass snakes are known to be dissuaded from eating crested newts because of this.

## Newt's nerve poison

The poison of the crested newt is not only unpleasant; but men who have tasted it have found it to be burning. A far more potent poison is that of the California newt. The poison is found mainly in the skin, muscles and blood of the newt, as well as in its eggs. Analysis showed that the poison is a substance called tetrodotoxin, which is also found in puffer fish. Tetrodotoxin extracted from newts' eggs is so powerful that $\frac{1}{3000}$ oz. can kill 7 000 mice. It acts on the nerves, preventing impulses from being transmitted to the muscles. Somehow, in a manner that is not understood, California newts are not affected by their own poison. Their nerves still function when treated with a solution of tetrodotoxin 25 000 times stronger than that which will completely deaden a frog's nerves.

| class | Amphibia |
|---|---|
| order | Caudata |
| family | Salamandridae |
| genera & species | *Taricha torosa* California newt *Triturus cristatus* crested newt *T. helveticus* palmate newt *T. vulgaris* smooth newt others |

△ *Underneath it all. Male smooth newt with its spotted front, from below.*
▽ *Just after take-off. Male crested newt with its crest and broad tail.*

▽ *Land bound. The red eft stage of the red spotted newt* **Diemictylus viridescens**. *After a few years they re-enter the water and turn dull green.*

P Morris

John Norris Wood

△ *Putting in the ground work: a palmate newt hauls itself over the rocks.*
▽ *Hooked up—by its tail: marbled newt* **Triturus marmoratus**.

△ *The outside cover: a perfectly cast newt skin.*
▷ *That loving approach. Alpine newts* **Triturus alpestris**.

Heather Angel

# Night adder

The four species of night adder belong to the viper family and are related to the common adder (p 13). They are probably more primitive than other vipers as they lay eggs instead of bearing their young alive. The scales on their heads are large, like the 'head shields' of the family Colubridae, which includes the egg-eating and hog-nosed snakes. Two of the night adders are also different from the other vipers, and indeed other venomous snakes, in that their poison glands extend back into the body. The glands may be as much as 4 in. long and are connected to the fangs by long ducts.

Night adders live in Africa, to the south of the Sahara desert in open country such as savannah. The common or rhombic night adder is very common in many localities, extending from the Cape to the Sudan and Somalia. The stout body with its fairly short tail is about 2 ft long but common night adders can grow to 3 ft. The scales are very smooth and the ground colour is light to dark grey or brown. Behind the head there is a dark V which points towards the snout, and running down the back there is a row of dark rhomboidal patches from which the snake gets its name. The snouted night adder of southern and eastern Africa is very similar in appearance to the common night adder except that the tip of the snout is turned up and it has a shorter body— usually 12—15 in.

The two other species are restricted to eastern Africa. The velvety-green night adder lives in Tanzania, Kenya and Uganda. Like the snouted night adder, the tip of the snout is upturned. It is grass-green above and whitish underneath, and has a V on the head and chevrons running down the back. Lichtenstein's night adder is confined to Uganda and western Kenya. It is olive-green with indistinct markings on the back. Both species grow to 18—20 in.

## Demon adder

These sluggish nocturnal snakes are quite often trodden on as they are often very common on open ground which has been cleared for human settlement. The resulting bites, however, are not serious as the poison is not very strong and even without treatment the symptoms of swelling, haemorrhage and fever are not usually very severe, unless the victim is a child or sick person or unless the snake has been allowed to hang on and inject large quantities. It has acquired its nickname 'demon adder' not so much because of its poisonous bites but because of its threats: it inflates its body and hisses, putting on a bold, blustering show.

## Diet of amphibians

Frogs and toads are unusual food for vipers but night adders eat large numbers and it is perhaps for this reason that they favour damp localities. Some writers have gone so far as to state that night adders eat nothing but frogs and toads but they do also eat rats and mice. The prey is usually swallowed headfirst, having been held while the venom takes effect.

## Adder's love dance

When the night adders mate, in early spring, the male approaches the female from behind, rubbing his chin and throat over her tail, and slowly jerking himself forward so that he moves along her body. The female at first is indifferent and continues to wind forward. Then she begins to move more slowly, throwing her body into loops with the male following every move. After a while the male wraps his tail around the female's body and twists so their cloacas are brought together. After mating they disengage and go their separate ways.

The eggs are laid in a clutch of one or two dozen which may take up to 4 months to hatch. In tropical parts of Africa several clutches may be laid in one year. These could result from one mating as the sperms are stored in the female's reproductive tract. One female night adder kept in solitary confinement produced four fertile clutches in 5 months.

## Tale of teeth

Snakes can be classified by their poison apparatus as well as by the more usual method of dividing them into families, where snakes with similar poison apparatus may not be at all closely related. Apart from the non-venomous snakes, there are three groups which are named after the form of their fangs. The opisthoglyphs have grooved fangs. Glyph is derived from the Greek for 'carving' and at one time meant 'groove'. These snakes are not usually very dangerous as they inject little poison when they bite, but the boomslang (p 269) can be an exception. The second group, the proteroglyphs, includes such dangerous snakes as the cobras, coral snakes and the water snakes. In these, the walls of the grooves are sometimes folded over to form canals through which the venom can flow. The vipers and pit-vipers, which include the rattlesnakes, have fangs which fold back when the mouth is shut. These snakes are the solenoglyphs. Their fangs are always tubular, like hypodermic needles. The night adders belong to this group but they are the only ones with a trace of a groove on their fangs, which suggests how the hypodermic fangs of the more typical solenoglyphs were derived, from fangs with open grooves, by the gradual fusion of the walls.

| class | **Reptilia** |
|---|---|
| order | **Squamata** |
| suborder | **Serpentes** |
| family | **Viperidae** |
| genus & species | ***Causus defilippii*** *snouted night adder* *C. lichtensteini* *Lichtenstein's night adder* *C. resimus velvety-green night adder* *C. rhombeatus* *common or rhombic night adder* |

▽ *A common or rhombic night adder gets its teeth into a red toad.*

▽ *Applied mathematics? A rhombic night adder makes a figure of eight.*

Anthony Bannister: NHPA

Joe B Blossom: NHPA

# Night heron

*The night herons are a group of herons closely related to the boatbill (p 252). They are medium-sized, and compared with other herons (p 1058), they have shorter legs and necks, and their bills are shorter and heavier.*

*The black-crowned night heron is one of the most cosmopolitan birds. It breeds in southern Europe, occasionally wandering northwards, in Africa and southern Asia. In America, it breeds from Canada to Tierra del Fuego and the Falklands and is also found in Hawaii. The plumage is generally grey, darker on the wings and glossy black on the back and crown. Three long white plumes trail from the back of the head. In southeast Asia, Australia and Polynesia, the black-crowned heron is replaced by the Nankeen night heron. This is bright chestnut with white underparts. The crown and nape are black and there are three white plumes. A white line runs through the eye, under which there is a patch of naked yellow-green skin.*

*Three other species live in America, including the whistling heron named after its high-pitched whistling call. The four Oriental night herons (genus Gorsachius) form a group separate from the other night herons. One species lives in Africa and the others in Asia. They resemble bitterns and nest solitarily rather than in colonies.*

▷ *Losing height. A black-crowned night heron drops gently down on its huge spreading wings.*

## Active at night

Night herons are aptly named as they are usually active in the evening when they can be heard calling as they fly from their roosts to the feeding places. In parts of the United States the black-crowned night heron is called the 'qwauk' or 'qwa-bird' from its guttural call. Its flight is more buoyant than the typical laboured beat of herons and the neck is held shortened rather than doubled back. During the breeding season night herons are more active in the day as they have to find extra food for their chicks.

## Fishy diet

Night herons feed mainly on small fish which they catch by standing motionless then stabbing with a rapid thrust of the bill. At other times they stalk through the water seeking less active prey. They fish in shallow water, usually about 6 in. deep, near the banks of pools, reed-beds and in ditches. Apart from fish, night herons eat frogs and other amphibians, shrimps, crabs, snails, worms and insects. Even small snakes and field mice may occasionally be caught.

## Sounds like murder

Apart from the Oriental night herons which nest solitarily, except where the terrain is particularly suitable, night herons nest in large colonies, with as many as 2 000 nests. There is usually one nest in each tree, but there may be as many as 12, and a single colony may cover many acres of woodland or thicket. At the height of the breeding season, when the colony is packed with adults and young, the noise has been described as being like '200 – 300 Indians choking or throttling each other'. The sight and sound of the colony is made more impressive because night herons often nest with egrets, ibises, cormorants and other species of heron.

M Brosselin: Jacana

# The night fishers

◁◁ *Still waiting. A Nankeen night heron waits motionless, ready to strike a passing fish with its spear-like bill. It does not usually impale the fish but grasps it firmly in its strong bill before swallowing it whole.*

△ *The community centre. A group of black-crowned night herons crowd together in the centre of their nesting colony which may cover several acres. They are tolerant birds, often nesting with other gregarious species.*

◁ *A night raider. A yellow-crowned night heron,* **Nyctanaffa violacea,** *struts about on the edge of the water in search of food. It usually fishes in shallow water and eats small amphibians and insects as well as fish.*

▽ *The nest inspector. A sleek black-crowned night heron calls on two well endowed African spoonbills* **Platalea alba** *to see if they are at home. If not he will plunder the nests for any unguarded chicks.*

MP Harris

Popperfoto

## It pays to advertise

During the breeding season the legs of night herons become tinged with red. The male chooses the nest site and starts to build the nest, at the same time advertising for a mate. The male attracts the female by his courtship dance in which he lowers his head and wings and 'marks time' on the branch. At intervals he lowers his head and utters a hissing call. When a female approaches, his head and neck feathers are erected, the three plumes are spread out so they are almost at right angles to each other, and the eyeballs are protruded to show off the red irises. He then lowers his bill and stretches out his neck towards the other bird. This 'greeting ceremony' is performed throughout the breeding season whenever the two partners meet, and they also caress each other with their bills.

The nest is a crude platform of twigs and reeds that is sometimes blown down in a high wind. It is usually built in trees or saplings growing in or overhanging water. The Nankeen night heron sometimes nests on the ground, arranging only sufficient sticks to prevent the eggs rolling about.

Three to five bluish-green eggs are laid and incubated by both parents for 3 weeks. Newly-hatched chicks are fed on liquid, digested food and after 3 weeks, on semi-digested fish and crustaceans. Later they can seize whole fish from the parents' bill and eventually the parents lay food on the nest for the chicks to pick up. When 2–3 weeks old the chicks can leave the nest and scramble among the branches but they do not fly until 6 weeks old.

## Luminous birds

In North America, if not elsewhere, night herons sometimes glow in the dark. A Texan naturalist, for instance, recorded how, at the age of 12, he saw 'balls of fire' in a swamp only 'a stone's throw away'. This must have been an eerie sight and probably no less eerie was the revelation, by a sheet of lightning, that the fire was coming from a night heron. In later years when the Texan saw these balls of fire his flashlight always revealed them to be night herons.

These are not the only birds to glow in the dark. Barn owls, ghostly enough with their white plumage and silent flight, are so often seen to glow that they have earned the local names of 'glim ullert' (shining owl), 'glimmer gowk' and 'lantern bird'. The cause of their glowing plumage is thought to be a luminous fungus that has brushed onto it while the owl was in a tree cavity, but no such explanation has been advanced for the luminous night herons.

| class | **Aves** |
|---|---|
| order | **Ciconiiformes** |
| family | **Ardeidae** |
| genera & species | **Gorsachius magnificus** *magnificent night heron* **Nycticorax caledonicus** *Nankeen night heron* **N. nycticorax** *black-crowned night heron* **N. sibilatrix** *whistling heron, others* |

# Nightingale

*Although one of the most famous bird singers and an inspiration to romantic poets from earliest times, the nightingale is unimpressive to look at. Male and female are alike, 6½ in. long, russet brown above, dull white tinged with brown below, and with a bright rufous tail and rump. The nightingale is more often heard than seen as it is a very shy bird that seldom emerges from the undergrowth when feeding.*

*The nightingale's summer range extends from England (south and east of a line joining the Wash and Severn) eastward across western Europe and the Mediterranean regions to the Balkans and Asia Minor, and southward to northwest Africa. On the outskirts of this range it is local and irregular. It arrives in Europe in spring and leaves at the end of August and during September, and winters in tropical Africa. There are two allied races in Asia which winter in East Africa.*

## Feeding on the ground

The nightingale frequents thick woodland undergrowth, thickets and scrubland and also damp, marshy spots where insects are plentiful. It feeds mainly on the ground, on worms, spiders and insects, especially beetles, and also the larvae of butterflies and moths and the pupae of ants. Fruit and berries are also taken.

## Speckled chicks

The male usually begins to display to the female in mid-April. He spreads out his rufous tail, rapidly moving it up and down, and flutters his wings with his head dipped. The bulky nest, built by the hen alone, is made chiefly of dead leaves, especially oak leaves, and is lined with dead grass and some hair. It is built on or a little above the ground in woods or thickets among the brambles and nettles or in hedges. The eggs, usually 4 or 5, are olive-green or olive-brown and are incubated by the hen alone for 13—14 days, but after hatching the young are fed by both male and female. They fledge after 11—12 days but are fed by the parents for some days after this. The young have a mottled, speckled appearance rather like young robins but with rufous-coloured tails. There is only one brood a year.

## A most famous songster

Tastes in bird-song differ and some people say the song of the blackbird or thrush is sweeter than that of the nightingale, but for sheer power of delivery, richness, variety and dramatic contrast the nightingale's song is supreme. To listen on a warm moon-lit night, when all other song-birds are silent, to the harsh notes intermingled with the sweet and then a single pleading piping note beginning softly and rising to a crescendo, leaves one in no doubt why so much sentiment has been lavished on the nightingale. The song seems much too loud to come from so small a bird. Sometimes, in

Eric Hosking

△ *Aggressive display of a nightingale. To get this unusual picture the photographer used a 'trade secret' of placing a dummy cuckoo near the nightingale's nest.*

John Markham

△ *A parent's task is never finished — a nightingale with a beak full of food for its young.*
▽ *One brood a year is enough for any nightingale when the chicks are as demanding as these.*

H Orth: Bavaria

the midst of the melody comes a harsh croak, which is also the alarm call. The nightingale sings mainly from mid-April to mid-June and although it sings habitually at night, it also sings in the day, but is less often heard then among all the other bird-song.

## Why at night?

The question is often asked: Why does the nightingale sing at night? Quite a number of birds can be heard at night, especially where there are powerful lights along a highway. Often a roosting bird will sing if it is disturbed. But few birds sing so consistently at night. Is it to advertise possession of a territory, the usual reason given for bird-song? If so, then we have to explain why a nightingale, unlike other song-birds, has such need of doing so at night. There is no evidence that nightingales maraud or try to dispossess each other at night, any more than do robins or blackbirds. There are no more dangers at night for nightingales than for other small song-birds. Indeed, whatever night predators there are, whether owls, or ground-prowlers such as foxes, or even rats, the song probably does nothing to diminish the dangers. It could be argued, of course, that by singing the male would draw the attention of a potential predator from the hen and nest. But nesting does not usually begin until mid-May, a full month after the singing has usually begun, and the song begins to die down in early June, soon after the young are hatched, and at the very time when any decoy-value it might have, would be greatest. No doubt parts of the nightingale's song serve some purpose, but it would be difficult to argue this for the whole song. It seems rather that the song is an expression of a seasonal rhythm, rising and falling coincidentally with the creative impulses of the body. It is influenced more by sunlight and temperature than by the presence or absence of rivals or enemies, and so far as nightingales are concerned they sing best on warm nights, and in a cold spring may not sing at all at night. Even a caged bird isolated from its natural world, and therefore from rivals, will sing. Is the song a form of artistic expression? Art in its simplest form depends upon an impulse to create. Once we can think of the nightingale's song in terms other than practical values, its coincidence with the zenith of the body's creative rhythm takes on a new significance. If a bird's reproductive glands did not wax and wane seasonally, presumably it would sing all the year round. We should then be less inclined to link it solely with breeding. We should be more inclined to think of it in terms of an art than of a utility. So, has song any aesthetic value for the nightingale itself? We cannot know but it is just possible that the nightingale may sometimes sing for the sheer joy of living. Some ornithologists at least take the view that it does.

| class | **Aves** |
|---|---|
| order | **Passeriformes** |
| family | **Turdidae** |
| genus & species | *Luscinia megarhynchos* |

# Nightjar

The nightjar, unlike the ideal child of Victorian days, is more often heard than seen. It starts to fly soon after sundown and is active throughout the night. By day its remarkable camouflage keeps it hidden. Yet despite this nightjars have probably been given more common names than any other bird. Fern-owl, churn-owl, eve-jarr, dorhawk, nighthawk are only a few of them. In South Africa a nightjar is called a brain-fever bird because its insistent churring through the night can drive nearby campers almost crazy. The most frequent name, and one appearing in many languages, is goatsucker.

The original nightjar or goatsucker, called **caprimulgus** (goatsucker) by the Romans, is the one that winters in Africa as far south as the Cape and spends its summers in North Africa, Europe and Asia. It is $10\frac{1}{2}$ in. long, its plumage is grey, barred and streaked with buff, chestnut and black, and its beak is small although the gape is very wide with strong bristles around the mouth. The adult male has white patches on the tail and wings.

There are 70 species all much alike in plumage and habits, including the American poor-will, whip-poor-will, chuck-will and night-hawks, which will be dealt with later. In southern Europe and western North Africa is the red-necked nightjar which has a distinctive reddish collar. The Egyptian nightjar, of southwest Asia and northern Africa, lives in deserts and is sandy-coloured. In eastern and southeast Asia are the jungle nightjar and the large-tailed nightjar. The long-tailed nightjar in Africa has very long central feathers in the tail. The pennant-winged nightjar, 11 in. long, has the innermost pair of primaries 2 ft. long, while the male standard-winged nightjar in the breeding season, has one bare-shafted feather in each wing 2 ft long and a 6 in. flag-like vane at the tip. In Australia the large-tailed, white-throated and spotted nightjars are similar to the European nightjar but larger.

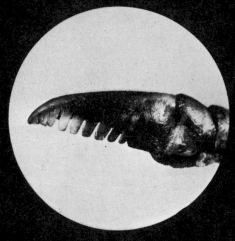

△ 'But the circumstance that pleased me most was that I saw it distinctly, more than once, put out its short leg while on the wing, and, by a bend of the head, deliver somewhat into its mouth. If it takes any part of its prey with its foot, as I have now the greatest reason to suppose it does these chafers, I no longer wonder at the use of its middle toe, which is curiously furnished with a serrated claw.' This is Gilbert White's explanation, in a letter written to Thomas Pennant in 1771, of the series of saw-like notches on the underside of the third toe of a nightjar.

◁ Sitting pretty — a European nightjar. During the day nightjars sit motionless among dead leaves and bracken camouflaged by their speckled, barred, brown and buff plumage.

▽ An evil stare from the large eye typical of a nocturnal animal — **Caprimulgus pectoralis**. Whether the bristles around the mouth act as organs of touch is not really known.

Opposite page: Protective husband — European nightjar hovers over his mate.

## Cloak of invisibility

The European nightjar is almost invisible during the day as it rests on the ground on heaths, bracken-covered slopes and open woodland. To say that its plumage harmonizes with its background is less correct than to say that its colours are so broken up that the bird defeats the eye and appears to dissolve into nothing. Whether the nightjar is among bracken, on lichens, on rocks or on sand it is almost impossible to see and one may almost tread on it before it moves. The invisibility is increased by the nightjar closing its eyes and watching an intruder through slits, so its large eyes do not give away its presence. By contrast, the rays of a torch shone into bushes at night may be reflected in a pair of red-glowing eyes suggestive of a large animal.

*Although it is normal for the white-throated nightjar to produce two broods each summer it was not until these photographs were taken that there was any evidence of an overlapping brood occurring in this species. During the day the parents incubated the second egg while concealing the hatched chick of the first brood. The second egg was laid exactly in the same spot as the first one.*

1 *The egg is laid on the ground unconcealed.*
2 *Both sexes take part in incubating the egg.*
3 *Chick hatches with a complete down cover.*
4 *18-day-old chick sits beside the second egg.*
5 *First chick threatens the photographer.*

1

2

3

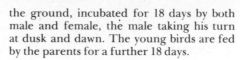
4

5

## Insect catcher number one

Nightjars become active at about sundown. They fly with a silent, almost moth-like flight, with strong, deliberate wingbeats alternating with graceful glides and easy wheeling movements. The characteristic churring or jarring call is heard most when the sky is clear. When the skies are overcast, the birds are silent. Nightjars call, almost invariably, perched lengthwise along a branch.

It used to be said that a nightjar flies with mouth agape, the bristles around the mouth acting as a sweepnet to catch insects or at least to direct them into the mouth. This is now disputed. Its food is almost wholly insects, from moths and large beetles to mosquitoes, but there are records of small birds being caught, perhaps accidentally. One nightjar examined had 500 mosquitoes in its stomach. Whether the bristles also act as organs of touch, as has been suggested, is problematical. On the third toe of a nightjar, on the undersurface, is a series of saw-like notches. This is used to comb the bristles around the mouth, and, so it is said, to remove the scales of moths that have been caught.

## Gun-shot wedding

The white patches on the wings and tail of the male stand out in courtship. This probably helps the recognition of the sexes. The male flies around the female in wide circles, either beating his wings or holding them stiffly and obliquely over his back, with his tail depressed and fanned. Every now and then he claps his wings with a sound like a pistol shot. Other nightjar males use their long feathers for display. The standard-winged nightjar, for example, holds his two flagged primaries vertically over his back, whereas in normal flight they are trailing. At the end of May the female lays two elliptical eggs, creamy white mottled with brown and purple. No nest is made. The eggs lie on the ground, incubated for 18 days by both male and female, the male taking his turn at dusk and dawn. The young birds are fed by the parents for a further 18 days.

## Drawing the enemy away

When disturbed at the nest the parent nightjar performs its distraction display, flopping over the ground as if with a broken wing. When this display is performed in the still of night the beating of the wings on the ground sounds uncannily loud. After the eggs are hatched the distraction display is still used to draw the attention of an intruder away from the young birds, which stay very still. Should the intruder go near the babies, however, they spread their wings, open wide their mouths and lunge at it—a disconcerting bluff.

## Egg-carrying parents

Audubon, the celebrated American ornithologist, described seeing a chuck-will, an American nightjar, remove its eggs with its mouth when danger threatened. He saw one of the pair wait beside two eggs that had been disturbed, then he saw the two parents each take an egg in their mouth and fly away with it. Audubon's story was long doubted but this same behaviour has been seen since in other species of nightjars. Moreover, nightjars are reported to carry their chicks held between their thighs, as do woodcocks.

# Do they suck goats?

Few birds show themselves in as many varying ways as nightjars. One may fly past your face in semi-darkness in smooth silent, almost ghost-like flight. A pair may circle over your head in courtship flight, when the crack of the male's wings has a startling, rather frightening quality, in the gathering gloom. In semi-desert parts of the world it is not unusual for a nightjar to be seen lying on the ground in the headlights of a car. Usually, even on the brightest moonlit night, it is impossible to see the bird or to track it as it moves from one perch to another, churring first here, then there, like a restless unseen spirit. It is not surprising therefore that some of the names given to nightjars show them to have been held in superstitious awe. The one name that has persisted over the last 2 000 years at least, in numerous languages and in many parts of the world, is goatsucker. The legend is that it takes milk from the udders of goats. This may be a fanciful allusion to the bird's wide gape. It may even have been a name that sprang from an entirely different source now obscured by the mists of time. It may even be true. After all, there have been the same stories for as long a time about hedgehogs, which have similarly been ridiculed but are now found to be almost certainly correct. Even Audubon's story of nightjars carrying away their eggs was for long met with scepticism.

| class | **Aves** |
|---|---|
| order | **Caprimulgiformes** |
| family | **Caprimulgidae** |
| genera & species | ***Caprimulgus aegyptius*** *Egyptian nightjar* |
| | ***C. europaeus*** *European nightjar* |
| | ***C. indicus*** *jungle nightjar* |
| | ***C. macrurus*** *large-tailed nightjar* |
| | ***C. ruficollis*** *red-necked nightjar* |
| | ***Eurostopodus mystacalis*** *white-throated nightjar* |
| | ***E. guttatus*** *spotted nightjar* |
| | ***Macrodipteryx longipennis*** *standard-winged nightjar* |
| | ***Scotornis climacurus*** *long-tailed nightjar* |
| | ***Semeiophorus vexillarius*** *pennant-winged nightjar, others* |

# Night lizard

*Night lizards look rather like geckos, and they also have a permanent 'spectacle', composed of a transparent scale, which covers each eye. The night lizards are a family found only in America. One genus **Xantusia** is found in the United States where some species are quite common in certain localities. The desert night lizard is found in the desert of California, Nevada, Utah, Arizona and Baja California where it lives in cover provided by Joshua trees and other species of Yucca. The maximum head and body length is 1¾ in. for males and 2 in. for females. Both have tails a little longer than the combined head and body length. The velvety skin is covered with fine scales on the upperparts and large square scales on the underparts. The colour varies from yellowish or grey to green, with black speckling on top, and pale grey to very light green underneath. The desert night lizard changes colour daily, being paler during the day than at night. The granite night lizard lives in California and is yellowish with black speckling. The island night lizard is found only on three small islands off the coast of California. The fourth of the night lizards found in the United States is the Arizona night lizard. Night lizards of two other genera **Gaigeia** and **Lepidophyma** live in Mexico and Central America, and one species **Cricosaura typica** lives in Cuba.*

## Living with wood rats

As their name implies night lizards are nocturnal, hiding by day and usually coming out to forage only at night. The desert night lizard is one of the commonest lizards in the southwest United States but until a short while ago it was regarded as being quite rare. This was before it was realised that desert night lizards were sheltering in Joshua trees. The fallen branches and dead clusters of leaves of Joshua trees present excellent cover in the desert from enemies and from the sun's rays. Other plants do not provide such good cover but on the fringes of the deserts night lizards hide under sagebrush. A favourite hiding place

△ *Always staring? A desert night lizard like all the other night lizards, lacks moveable eyelids. The eye is covered by a clear scale derived from the lower lid.*

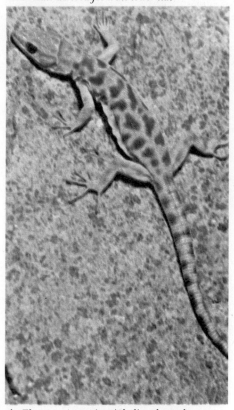

△ *Flat out. A granite night lizard crawls over a rock—its natural habitat.*
▽ *An island night lizard with the bluntly pointed head that is typical of these lizards.*

of desert night lizards is in the nests wood rats build at the bases of the Joshua trees. The nests consist of piles of sticks and leaves which may be 2 ft high and 4 ft across, so providing very good cover. The lizards may make their homes in them while the wood rats are still in residence. In the summer night lizards lie up under a log or pile of leaves usually in single pairs but in winter they may gather in groups of up to 40 or more.

Other night lizards live in rock crevices or among boulders. The granite night lizard lives under slabs that have flaked off the bedrock and the Cuban night lizard lives among loose limestone boulders.

### Feeding in leaf litter

Joshua trees also supply the desert night lizard with a plentiful source of food because night lizards feed on small animals that live in leaf litter and under logs. Ants, beetles and flies are their favourite food but they also take moths, beetles, spiders and sometimes scorpions.

### Egg-tube placenta

Night lizards are viviparous, their young being born alive. After fertilisation the eggs take 90–120 days to develop. During this time food passes to the developing embryos and excretory products pass back to the mother through a placenta formed from the joining of the embryonic membranes and the oviduct. The litter is very small consisting usually of two young and never more than three. They are born in September or October and measure just under 1 in.

## Change of shift

The desert night lizard's habits of hiding under cover and emerging mainly at night would seem to be an ideal way of life for an animal living in hot, dry country, although most desert reptiles are active during the day and retire to shelter at night.

A close study of the desert night lizard has shown that it probably was once similar to other lizards in its habits. It has vertical pupils like those of day-living reptiles, and it reacts to temperature changes in the same way as the bearded lizard and other day-living reptiles. It still likes to bask in the sun, but as its habitat became hotter and drier it has taken to hiding during the day in the cover provided by the Joshua trees. These trees are now rapidly diminishing in numbers but fortunately land has been set aside to preserve the stands of Joshua trees, and with them, incidentally, one of North America's most unusual reptiles.

| class | **Reptilia** |
|---|---|
| order | **Squamata** |
| suborder | **Sauria** |
| family | **Xantusidae** |
| genera & species | ***Cricosaura typica*** *Cuban night lizard* ***Xantusia vigilis*** *desert night lizard* **X. henshawi** *granite night lizard* **X. arizonae** *Arizona night lizard* **X. riversiana** *island night lizard* |

# Nile fish

*There are several fishes living in the Nile and in rivers in tropical West Africa that can swim backwards and forwards with equal ease. Little notice was taken of this until, within the last 20 years, it was found that each fish can generate its own electric field. One of these is **Gymnarchus niloticus**, which has been called the Nile fish but is more often called by its scientific name, as it is of special interest to students of biology.*

*The Nile fish is 6 in. long, flattened from side to side and ending behind in a slender 'rat's tail'. The only fins it has are a pair of very small pectorals and a long ribbon-like dorsal fin starting just behind the head and ending well short of the slender tip of the body. The head is rounded with small eyes, blunt snout, wide mouth and strong teeth. Its body is covered with very small scales.*

*The other species, belonging to the family Mormyridae are more 'fish-shaped'. The body is compressed and while the pelvic fins are absent and the pectoral fins small, both dorsal and anal fins are well-developed and the anal fin is usually longer than the dorsal. The tail fin is forked. Some species have a finger-like process on the jaw which is used as a feeler for searching for small animal food in the mud. Others have a long proboscis-like snout which gives the fishes a most unusual appearance. Mormyrids swim by waving the dorsal and anal fins and keeping the body rigid. Like the Nile fish, they also have a weak electric system which they use to sense their surroundings.*

*The Nile fish ranges from the upper reaches of the River Nile to the Chad basin and beyond to Senegal and the basin of the Niger river. The mormyrid fishes occupy much the same area but also spread into the Congo.*

## Plugging into a fish

The most remarkable discovery of an electric field surrounding the Nile fish was first published in 1951 by Dr HW Lissmann, of Cambridge University. Muscles on either side of the tail form electric generators which throughout the life of the fish are constantly giving out pulses at the rate of 300 a second. Lissmann found that when he lowered a pair of electrodes, connected to an oscilloscope, into the water containing a Nile fish, these electric discharges were picked up. Each discharge spreads out through the surrounding water forming an electric field like the field around a bar magnet, with the positive pole at its head and the negative pole at its tail. Any object in the water disturbs the field as when the two ends of a U-shaped copper wire were dipped into the field near the fish. The fish was disturbed and swam away, but would remain still and undisturbed if a similarly shaped non-conducting material were lowered into the water.

△ *An elephant-trunk fish, **Gnathonemus petersi**. This species has only its lower lip elongated. The mormyrids and gymnotids, although not closely related, have some very similar behavioural characteristics. Both can swim backwards and forwards and both have electric organs.*

Carlo Bevilacqua

## Surrounded by an electric field

Later it was found that the sense-organs with which the fish picked up the disturbances are minute jelly-filled pits in the skin of the head, each with a receptor at the bottom. These are like the lateral line sense-organs of other fishes. The sensitivity of these organs is such that, as Lissmann has said: 'combing one's hair with a vulcanite comb and waving such an electrified insulator near an aquarium containing these fishes causes much excitement amongst the inhabitants'. They will also respond to a bar magnet placed near the aquarium. Conditioning experiments were carried out in which two porous clay tubes were put in the aquarium, one filled with tap water or some other conductor, the other with a non-conductor such as wax or glass. The fish was trained to come to the conducting tube by rewarding it with a piece of meat. It soon learned to come to the conducting tube and to ignore the non-conductor. By changing around the contents of the clay tubes the sensitivity of the Nile fish could be shown. It was, for example, able to detect the presence in a tube of a glass rod $\frac{1}{12}$ in. diameter, which would cause only a minute change in the fish's electric field. When the fish's own discharges were recorded and played back it attacked the electrodes, as if they were one of its fellows.

## A fish that cannot bend

The electric field enables the Nile fish to detect the small fishes on which it feeds without seeing them. It has little use for eyes anyway in the muddy waters of the swamps in which it lives. With the electric field the fish can move backwards as well as forwards with confidence because it can detect obstacles in its path. It swims in a smooth glide with a rigid body, driven by a wave passing through the long dorsal fin. A Nile fish swimming forward merely reverses the direction of the wave to swim backwards. The rigid body is necessary, for were it to move the body, as most fishes do, this would disturb the electric field around it.

## Floating home

The Nile fish makes a floating four-sided nest of grass and other pieces of plant, with three sides out of the water and the fourth submerged to a depth of 4–8 in. The female lays about 1 000 large amber-coloured eggs. The larvae have long gill filaments and the remains of the yolk-sac are still attached. They stay in the shelter of the nest for 5 days, by which time the yolk is used up and the baby fishes are then 3 in. long.

## Sacred 'elephant trunks'

How the Nile fish interprets the messages from the sense-organs, to tell the position of an obstacle or other object is not yet known. The part of the brain linked to the sense-organs is very large so we can suppose it is able to analyse the complicated data coming from the sense-organs. The mormyrids also have large brains, said to bear the same proportion to the body as the human brain. Those who have kept these fishes in aquaria tell of their playing for hours on end with a leaf or a ball of tinfoil. They also turn on their backs and glide alternately backwards and forwards. We do not normally think of fishes playing in this manner and it reminds us of some of the antics of needlefishes (see p 1561). Whether it was the curious 'elephant trunk' of some of the mormyrids, or whether it was their playfulness that caught the attention of the Ancient Egyptians, nobody can say. The fact remains, however, that as early as 2 500 BC mormyrids were painted on the murals in tombs and figured on bas-reliefs.

| | |
|---|---|
| class | **Pisces** |
| order | **Mormyriformes** |
| family | **Gymnarchidae** |
| family | **Mormyridae** |

# Electric generator

▷ *Pattern of electric field of* **Gymnarchus.** *The electric generating organs are in the rear end of the body while the electric sensory organs are in the head region. The fish responds to changes in the distribution of electric potential over the body surface.*

▽ **Gymnarchus niloticus** *rises to the water surface to breathe. This series of photographs clearly shows how the fish swims with graceful ease propelled by the undulating fin along its back. It does not lash its tail from side to side as most other fish do, but keeps its spine straight. It keeps its body rigid so as not to disturb the electric field generated in the tail. The tail of this remarkable fish is naked, and it is from this characteristic the fish gets its name, for 'gymnarchus' means 'naked tail'.*

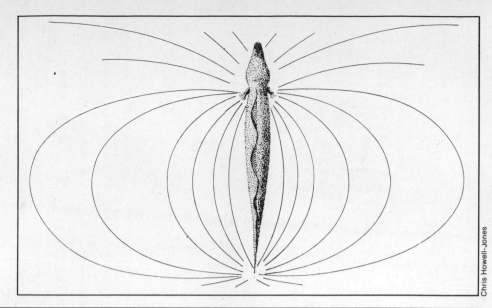

*Gene Wolfsheimer*

# Nile perch

*This is the largest freshwater fish in Africa and one of the largest perch-like fish in the world. Known as the king of African fish, it has a special interest for anglers and fishermen as a game fish, as well as being a giant with highly palatable flesh.*

*The Nile perch is stout bodied, high in the back, with a relatively small head. The eyes are large and the lower jaw juts forward beyond the upper jaw. The body is covered with large scales and the gill-covers bear prominent spines. The pectoral fins lie just behind the gills and immediately beneath them are the spiny pelvic fins. The dorsal fin is in two lobes, the front one having stout spiny rays. The first 3 rays of the anal fin are stout and spiny. The tail fin is rounded. The adult Nile perch is dull brown, olive or grey on the back, uniformly coloured or marbled, and silvery on the belly. The maximum size is in doubt: it is up to 6 ft long, possibly much more, with a weight of 266 lb, possibly up to 280 lb.*

*Although it is called the Nile perch, and ranges from Lake Albert to the Nile delta, it also lives in Lakes Chad, Rudolf and Abbaya (Congo) and the Senegal, Niger and Congo rivers. For reasons unknown it is absent from the Zambesi and other African rivers.*

## Sporting fish

A well-grown Nile perch is an extremely powerful fish, so much so that when hooked, it cannot be pulled to the surface. One method used by local fishermen is to tie the line to the end of the canoe and let the fish tire itself out. It is said to tow a canoe several miles, perhaps for as long as 2 hours, before it is exhausted. Little else is known about its habits: during the day the large adults lie in water 15–20 ft or more deep, coming into the shallows to feed at night. It is difficult to keep the fish alive in aquaria. They seem to settle in and feed well at first, then they die off. A good deal of research is going into this now but it is too early to give the results of it.

## Bigger and bigger meals

The Nile perch has something of the voracity of pike. Even the young fishes are cannibalistic. The manner of feeding of the two fishes is, however, different. Fishes like the pike, that have large teeth, open their mouths in a grin. The Nile perch has large numbers of tiny, backwardly directed, teeth arranged in broad bands. The teeth are too small to pierce the skin of prey. Instead they form a friction pad for holding it. Predatory fishes with small teeth have round mouths instead of long mouths that open in a pike-like grin.

The baby Nile perch begin to feed on plankton and later on freshwater prawns as well. Then, when about 4 in. long, they start feeding on tiny fish, eating larger and larger fish as they grow bigger. The large adults seldom eat anything smaller than a foot-long

*△ Baby Nile perch with an adult's aggressive nature, jutting lower jaw and stout body. Even the young fish is carnivorous, first feeding on plankton, then freshwater prawns, finally fish, eating larger and larger fish as it grows bigger and bigger.*

tiger fish and medium-sized Nile perch feed also on cichlids. It has been suggested that the perch might be introduced to other large African lakes where it does not occur naturally. There are, however, fears about what might happen to the other fishes which are at present an important food supply.

## Slow start in life

The adult females are more than twice the size of the males, with an average weight of 60 lb against an average of 25 lb in the males. The eggs are small, $\frac{1}{30}$ in. diameter, with a single oil globule, so they float just under the surface. They are only slightly heavier than water and the slightest movement in the water is enough to keep them buoyed up. Spawning takes place in relatively still waters: in lakes, in the oxbow lakes of rivers, or in flooded backwaters. The eggs hatch in less than 20 hours, so the larvae are at an early stage of development, being hardly more than embryos, and only $\frac{1}{20}$ in. long. When $\frac{1}{3}$ in. long they begin to look like normal fish larvae, with the yolk sac still attached. When $\frac{1}{2}$ in. long they begin to have the features seen in the adults but the body is marked with irregular dark bands. The only information on the life span is that a 165 lb specimen gave scale readings suggesting it was 12–18 years old.

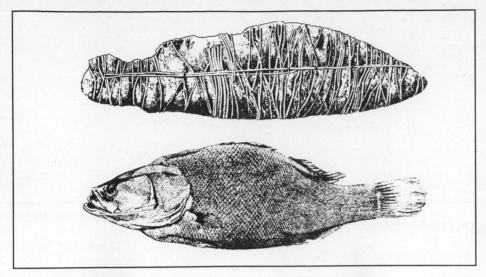

# Earliest mummified fish

The Nile perch was venerated and mummified by the Ancient Egyptians. At Esneh, in Upper Egypt, it was worshipped as a divinity of first rank, so much so that the Greeks called the town Latopolis, the City of the Lates fish. There, in the valley of the Nile, at the beginning of this century large numbers of the fish were dug out of the ground embalmed in brine, wrapped in cloth and tied with cords. The dry sandy soil doubtlessly helped to preserve them. Although over 2 500 years old, the flesh was in as good condition as fish cured in the sun today. Chemical analysis showed that the mummified fish contained as much animal matter as dried cod. Even the eyeballs were in good condition. At Gurob, about 60 miles south of Cairo, were other extensive burials, but these fish had been preserved in ashes or wrapped in grass and only their skeletons remain.

Paintings of the Nile perch were found in Egyptian tombs. It also figured on Greek coins. Towards the end of the 19th century a bronze model of the fish, $4\frac{1}{2}$ in. long, was found in Egypt. It contained the remains of a baby Nile perch, reduced to a small pile of bones but still recognizable as belonging to this species.

The extent to which the fish was venerated is shown by the way each fish was usually buried in its own pit. If two were buried together they were placed head to head or side by side; if more than two, they were arranged in layers. The great respect in which they were held is shown by the fact that no other animal was buried in the same pit as a Nile perch.

| class | **Pisces** |
|---|---|
| order | **Perciformes** |
| family | **Centropomidae** |
| genus & species | *Lates niloticus* |

*The Ancient Egyptians were animal worshippers and one animal they did not overlook was the fish we know today as **Lates niloticus**. Many mummified remains of **Lates** are scattered throughout the valley of the Nile. The top illustration is of a mummified Nile perch from Esneh, Upper Egypt, found buried at a shallow depth in sand. Examination of a mummy has shown that the fish had an incision made in its abdomen to allow the mummifying solution to enter the body. It was then immersed in a strong brine for a long time and finally swathed in linen cloths secured by a cord first wound around the body and then wound longitudinally. The mummified fish was then buried in dry sand. The illustration below this mummy is of a mummified **Lates** that has been unwrapped and cleaned of the dry salty slime in which it was pickled. Even after 25 centuries the fish is still perfectly preserved with intact scales, fins and eyeballs. There are also paintings of **Lates** on the walls of various tombs in Egypt. On the south wall of the tomb of Rahotep at Medum in Lower Egypt is a painting of a Nile perch carried on the handle of a boat paddle. Fisherman's tale come true (bottom). The same method is still used in Africa today.*

Arthur Christiansen

# Nilgai

The nilgai, also spelt nylghai or nylgau, is the largest Indian antelope. The bulls are 52—56 in. high and may weigh 600 lb, the females being considerably smaller. Only the male has horns, which are small, averaging 8 in. long. The nilgai's build is somewhat unusual, with the withers considerably higher than the rump. The male is blue-grey, the female and young tawny, and both have a white ring below each fetlock, two white spots on either cheek, and a short, stiff black mane. The lips, chin, inside of the ears and underside of the tail are white, and the males have a tuft of stiff black hair on the throat.

Closely related to the nilgai is the chousingha, or four-horned antelope, also of India. The males are 25 in. high and 37—45 lb weight. They have two pairs of horns; the front pair, $\frac{1}{2}$—1 in. long, is above the eyes, and the rear pair 3—4 in. long is in the usual place. The females are similar to the males but do not have horns. The dull red-brown coat is white below, fading to yellowish with age. There is a dark stripe down the front of each leg. Chousinghas carry their long, tufted tails tucked between their legs.

Nilgai browse or graze in hilly country which is sparsely covered with trees, or among the long grass and scrub of the plains. They range from the base of the Himalayas to Mysore but they are not found in East Bengal, Assam or on the Malabar coast.

Nilgai live in the glades in open forest or parkland where they browse on the shrubs and fruit. The cows and calves are not at all shy and are easy to approach as the photographers of these pictures have discovered. Even the young nilgai (above, with mother, and below) have the white patches characteristic of this large Indian antelope. A cow (opposite page) poses patiently for the camera, her striking features shown to full advantage.

Popperfoto

G Bodmer: Bavaria

Ron Boardman

◁ The name 'nilgai' means 'blue cow', but the cow is in fact tawny coloured. It is the male that has a bluish coat. Only the male has horns which are 8in. long so appearing very stunted. Both cow and bull have a small neck mane and the distinctive white patches.
▽ A close relative of the nilgai is the chousingha or four-horned antelope, also found in India. Again it is only the male that has horns, but the chousingha has two pairs. One pair, ½ in. long, are above the eyes, the other pair, 3 in. long, are in the usual place.

Aldo Margiocco

### Related yet unlike in habits

Nilgai are creatures of habit; within their home ranges, the herds of 4–10 always use set places for resting, drinking and defaecation. They build up big dung-heaps, like those of rhinoceroses, which probably serve the same purposes: to mark the centre of the home range and enable wandering bulls to identify the sex of the occupants. The herds are made up of a few cows with their young, and one or two young bulls just turning grey; the adult bulls are solitary or live in small groups. The small cow-calf groups sometimes join temporarily where their home ranges meet. Nilgai will often drop to their knees when they are grazing, as their necks are short. Sometimes they cause considerable damage to crops. They feed mainly in the early morning and late evening, lying up in shade during the heat of the day. Although their trips to water are regular, some go for long periods without water when sources dry up.

The four-horned antelope has a similar distribution to the nilgai, but extends a little further east. It too lives more in hilly country, in the thicker cover of woodlands, but not in forests. Like the nilgai it shelters during the heat of the day, in tall grass and open jungle, and feeds mainly in the morning and evening. Unlike the nilgai, however, it is very dependent on water, and drinks regularly, establishing its home range near standing water, on the edge of the jungle— even near a village watering tank! Four-horned antelope live singly or in pairs, or a buck may gather 4 or 5 does around him.

Two or more does with their young may get together, but these associations are not permanent. The females appear to have home ranges, and, like the nilgai, they build up dung-heaps in them.

### Awkward but speedy

Both nilgai and chousingha walk and run rather jerkily. The nilgai with its long legs has a stilty gallop. When threatened, chousingha dive into the undergrowth but the nilgai herd give low alarm grunts and gallop off slouchingly, with their heads held up, as if stargazing. Their awkwardness is, however, deceptive. They run as fast as a horse and can go over much rougher ground. Nevertheless, they are preyed upon by leopard, tiger, wolf and dhole, but are not usually molested by man because they look so like cows, which are held sacred. Both species are easily tamed when young.

### He kneels to conquer

During the rut the males compete to join the females' herds. They drop to their knees, pressing their foreheads together, and wrestle, or push with their necks. Although young nilgai have been seen at all seasons, the usual mating time is March to April, at least in northern India. The 2 young are born 8–9 months later, in November and December, and are sexually mature at 18 months. Four-horned antelope rut during the rainy season, in summer, and the 1–3 young are born in January or February, after about 8 months. This is a long gestation for such a small antelope.

## Of ancient stock

Both nilgai and chousingha belong to the 'bovine' group of antelopes, closely related to cattle and buffaloes. Their nearest relatives among antelopes are the African bushbuck, kudu and eland. According to the palaeontologist Pilgrim, they are very primitive, and have hardly changed since Miocene times, 15 million years ago. They are in fact extremely closely related to the group from which the cattle arose. Unlike the bushbuck and its relatives, nilgai and chousingha share some important skull characteristics with cattle and buffaloes. They have a long palate, their molar teeth have extra pillars on them and high crowns, and they have symmetrically shovel-shaped incisors. Also, they lack the elaborately twisted horns of bushbuck and eland antelopes, which have asymmetrical incisors and no accessory columns on the molars. Primitive ancestors of living cattle and buffaloes had horns in the male only— like the nilgai and chousingha. Finally the colour-patterns of nilgai and some cattle, such as the anoa, are strikingly similar, even to the two spots on the cheek!

| class | **Mammalia** |
|---|---|
| order | **Artiodactyla** |
| family | **Bovidae** |
| genera & species | ***Boselaphus tragocamelus*** nilgai ***Tetracerus quadricornis*** four-horned antelope |

# Noctiluca

*When the surface of the sea gives out a ghostly light and flashes and flames at the stroke of an oar, or the breaking of a wave, noctiluca may be responsible. This is a single-celled animal, but an exceptionally large one as it is usually $\frac{1}{50} - \frac{1}{25}$ in. across, and sometimes as much as $\frac{1}{8}$ in. Other organisms can produce a similar luminescence, including others of the dinoflagellates, the group to which noctiluca belongs. Most dinoflagellates obtain their energy by photosynthesis and are therefore regarded as plants, but noctiluca leads a purely animal existence and has none of the pigments needed to utilise the sun's rays. Here, as is so often the case with single-celled organisms, the distinction between animal and plant is blurred.*

*Noctiluca is roughly spherical and its surface is covered by a thick outer layer or pellicle, and indented on the side that floats uppermost. From this upper side, like the stalk on a cherry, springs a tentacle, flattened and cross-striated, and about as long as the body is wide. Close to its base are grouped the other most important structures, including a rod-like thickening of the surface layer, the 'mouth' with a 'lip' and a tiny flickering flagellum of uncertain function. Beneath the surface at this spot is the nucleus and from this region and across the interior of the sphere to its periphery stretch threads of cytoplasm that branch and rejoin at intervals and in which oil droplets and other particles are carried along in a streaming motion. The cytoplasm may be colourless, blue-green or tinged with yellow, and between the strands is a semi-fluid sap.*

*There is only one species of noctiluca, known variously as **N. scintillans** and **N. miliaris** though the latter name is now taken to be correct.*

### Fiery soup

Noctiluca occurs in warm and temperate shallow coastal waters and at times the numbers floating near the surface may be enough to turn the sea into soup. It is then that the best displays of pyrotechnics can be seen. Noctiluca does not swim actively though the languid beating of the tentacle about half a dozen times a minute does tend to rotate it. The main function of the tentacle seems to be to capture food of planktonic organisms such as diatoms and copepod larvae. As it waves about, the prey is caught on its sticky surface and transferred to the mouth, with the help of the lip and another little structure nearby. Undigested particles are later discharged through the mouth.

### Dividing to multiply

Reproduction may be sexual or asexual. In asexual reproduction the animal simply splits in two, the group of structures at the upper pole disappearing temporarily, to be reformed in each of the two daughter cells.

This takes 12 to 24 hours. Sexual reproduction starts with the production of small 'swarmers', each one swimming by means of a flagellum. The swarmers, budded off in large numbers from the upper polar region, are attached at first but then swim off and leave the parent body to die. They join together in pairs but what happens after this fertilisation process is not clear.

### Chemical light

The word 'noctiluca' or 'night-light' was at one time a general term for nocturnal luminescence and was used in this way before it became associated with a particular organism. Moreover, various explanations for the nature of the light at sea had been put forward before its organic nature was known. In the 17th century people explained it as due to the rubbing together of salt particles like flints, the emission at night of light absorbed during the day; or to the friction of the waves with the atmosphere or with solid objects. Not until the middle of the 18th century were the 'luminous water insects' that we now know as noctiluca described and recognised as a source of the luminescence. At first they were thought to be jellyfish rather than Protista. Shortly afterwards, another of the sources of light was seen in the Mediterranean, a true luminous jellyfish *Pelagia noctiluca*. The light given out by noctiluca is produced only in certain granules in the cytoplasm and is given out in brief flashes when the organism is stimulated. The emission of light by the separate granules is not simultaneous, but spreads as a wave from the upper pole and is accompanied by electrical changes at the surface.

▽ *Plankton eats plankton—noctiluca ingests the larva of the brittle star **Ophiothrix fragilis**. Noctiluca waves its tentacle about to catch prey on the sticky surface (about 200 × life size).*

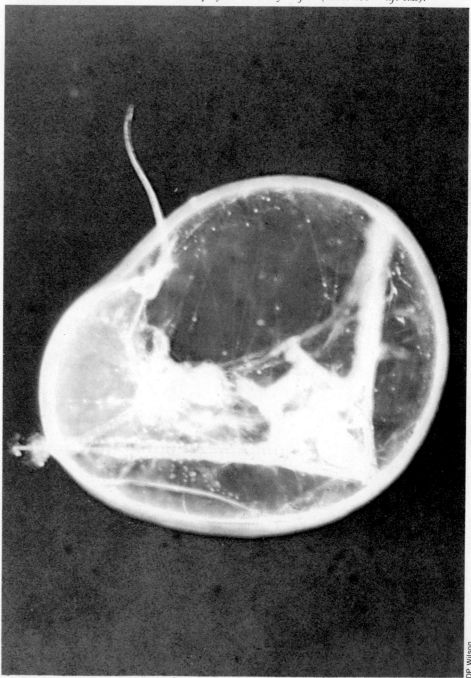

DP Wilson

## Chemical buoyancy

Life is so abundant in the upper layers of the oceans that buoyancy must not be thought of as a problem, though most living matter containing the usual salts and organic substances will tend to sink unless there is something, like the gas in nautilus (p 1558) and the swimbladders of many fish, to buoy it up. The cytoplasm of noctiluca is no exception. The cell as a whole can float because of the large volume of less dense sap between the strands of cytoplasm. The large size of these single-celled organisms, like the large size of a balloon or bathyscaphe, is perhaps related to the need for a great bulk of buoyant material. Fat men float better than lean men and in 1893 the suggestion was made that noctiluca owed its low density to its fat content. While this idea is now known to be incorrect, it is still not known exactly what makes the sap buoy-

ant. There is evidence that light ammonium and chloride ions replace heavier sodium and sulphate ions in the sap to some extent, but whether this is enough to explain the buoyancy of the sap is not settled. A curious feature of the sap that may be relevant is that it is usually acid (pH 3—4.6) and it is interesting that in certain squids the density of the tissues is offset by a large volume of low-density fluid in the body containing ammonium rather than sodium salts which is also unusually acid.

| | |
|---|---|
| phylum | **Protista** |
| class | **Mastigophora** |
| order | **Dinoflagellida** |
| family | **Noctilucidae** |
| genus & species | *Noctiluca miliaris* |

## Night light that scintillates

*An appropriate description of this sparkling protistan, for this is what **Noctiluca scintillans** means, although it is now usually known by the specific name **miliaris.***

▷ *Jewels of the sea. Enlarged to about 130 × life size a cluster of noctiluca look like glittering floating jewels.*

▽ *Noctiluca soup — the Research Vessel 'Sarsia' passes through a swarm of noctiluca. This luminescent dinoflagellate is noted for the way it tints the sea surface pink in the daytime and lights it up at night. To see these displays does not mean a voyage across the world, for they are much in evidence even in the English Channel.*

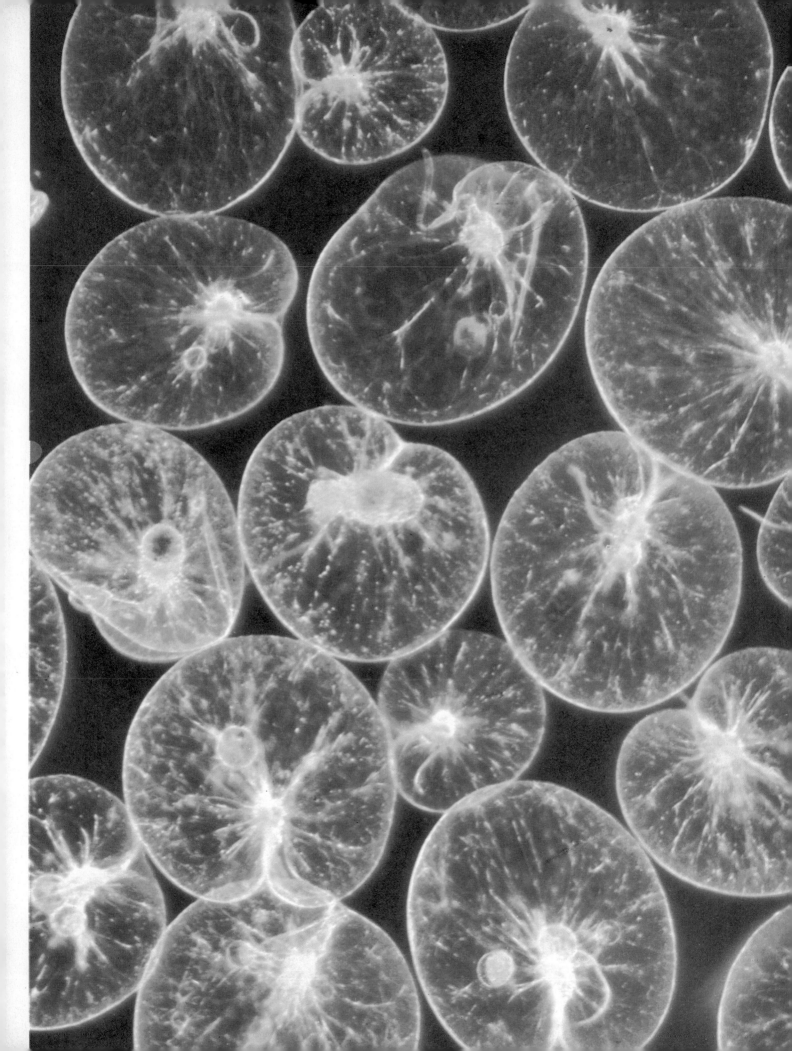

# Noddy

*Like other terns, the noddies are delicately built, about 12—16 in. long with slender wings, pointed bills and short legs. There are five species. The black or lesser noddy is 15½ in. long with dark brown, sometimes nearly black plumage except a pale, almost white cap running from the base of the bill and over the top of the eye, and under the eye there is a distinct white mark. The slightly larger brown, greater or common noddy has similar plumage, but the other noddies have lighter plumage and the white noddy or fairy tern, the smallest of the genus, is pure white except for eyes, bill and feet. The grey noddy is almost all grey except for black rings around the eyes. It is confined to the Pacific Ocean from Hawaii to Easter Island, while the other noddies are found in most tropical and subtropical seas.*

## Inaccessible nests

Noddies spend much of their time at sea and usually nest on inaccessible cliffs on fairly remote islands where there have not been many opportunities to study them. Between 1957 and 1959 the black, brown and white noddies were, however, studied in detail by members of a British Ornithologists' Union Expedition to Ascension Island. Although the ornithologists could reach only a few noddy nests and ring the occupants, it was possible to watch events at the nests. These noddies are of particular interest because they nest on cliffs, unlike other terns which generally nest on flat ground. Elsewhere, noddies nest in trees and bushes. In British Honduras, for instance, black noddies nest in mangroves and sometimes on the ground. On Ascension Island the noddies occupy the nesting ledges all the year round, but clutches are early in the year.

## Swooping for fish

Unlike their relatives, noddies do not plunge-dive (see black-headed gulls, p 225) but feed on the small, surface-living fish without entering the water. They swoop from about 20 ft up and catch the fish or squid when they are just under the surface. Anchovies, flying fish and squid form the bulk of their diet. Quite often noddies feed with other seabirds that do dive, catching the fish as they come to the surface or even as they leap into the air to try to escape from the other birds. They have also been seen congregating over shoals of tuna as these predatory fish force small fishes to take desperate measures to avoid being eaten. Noddies usually catch fish about 3 in. long but they have been seen bringing fish as much as 7 in. long back to their chicks.

## Shortage of housing

When noddies nest on cliffs there is often competition for suitable ledges where the eggs and chicks can be reared, even when there seem to be many suitable ledges on the cliffs. This is because noddies like to nest close together, so in each colony some pairs have to make do with poor sites and

▽ *Egg bound. A common noddy stands guard over its single egg. The exposed egg, normally protected by a nest, has been laid in a natural depression in the cliff rock.*

▽ *A productive tree. Noddies sitting on their untidy nests of leaves and twigs. They are part of a large colony of these birds nesting on Heron Island in the Great Barrier Reef.*

*△ Sooties and noddies gather to breed on Pelsart Island off Western Australia.*
*▽ A white capped noddy **Anous minutus** in a sticky situation. Its nest is stuck together with guano.*

risk losing their eggs or chicks. The housing situation is somewhat eased by the gradual accumulation of guano on the ledges and by the efforts of the noddies themselves in building nests of guano bound by feathers, seaweed or leaves. But such 'artificially' widened ledges are not completely safe!

Noddies lay a single egg, whereas most other terns lay two or three. Incubation takes about 5 weeks and is shared by both parents who take it in turns to incubate for 1—2 days. When the chicks hatch they are covered in down. The chicks of black noddies have the same pattern of dark brown and white as their parents, but those of brown noddies may be one of a variety of colours from dirty white to brownish black. The adults feed the chicks on fish and squid which they pass directly to the chick rather than dropping it on the ledge. The chicks fly when 7—9 weeks old. Those that grow up on ledges have to fly well from the start but if raised on bushes or fairly flat ground they can make practice flights. The chicks belonging to early broods on Ascension Island stand a better chance of survival than those hatched later because there is a shortage of food in the autumn.

### Safety on ledges

When they nest in bushes or on the ground noddies sometimes fall prey to cats or rats that have been introduced to their island homes, but they are safe on the cliff ledges where even the predatory frigatebirds are unable to reach them because of the difficulty of landing on a narrow ledge. Noddies are not defenceless either, and will swoop at intruders, stabbing them with their bills.

## Cliff-hangers

The kittiwake (p 1244) is a gull that has taken to nesting on inaccessible cliff ledges and some of its habits have changed as a consequence. It is less open to predation so its nests are not camouflaged and alarm calls are rarely given. On the other hand, the chicks have to avoid falling out of the nests. The noddies are terns that have taken to nesting on cliffs and they show the same pattern of changes as the kittiwake. There is a solid nest to contain the egg and chick and food is passed directly to the chick instead of being dropped. In this way it is neither lost nor left to foul the nest. Chicks of the white noddy have very sharp claws like kittiwake chicks, and very young chicks can hang upside down from one's finger. The noddies are not so completely adapted for cliff life as the kittiwake, however, perhaps because they sometimes nest on trees, bushes or flat ground. The white noddy, for instance, has camouflaged eggs and chicks, in common with other terns and most other members of the gull family.

| class | **Aves** |
|---|---|
| order | **Charadriiformes** |
| family | **Laridae** |
| genus & species | ***Anous albivittus*** *grey noddy* <br> ***A. albus*** *white noddy* <br> ***A. stolidus*** *brown noddy* <br> ***A. tenuirostris*** *black noddy* |

1553

△ *Nosing around — a numbat searches for termites among fallen eucalyptus leaves. It can extend its slender tongue for at least 4 in.*

Graham Pizzey; Photo Res

# Numbat

*Sometimes called the banded ant-eater or marsupial ant-eater, it is better to call this termite-eating animal the numbat, the name given it by the Aborigines. Although it is almost always said to eat termites and ants it now seems certain that it eats only termites. The numbat, up to 18 in. long, of which 7 in. is bushy tail, is reddish-yellow to chestnut-red with white bands around the body. The stout body is flattened across the hindquarters. Its muzzle is long and pointed and there is a black line running from the ear through the eyeline to the tip of the nose. Its skull is long and flattened and it has 52 teeth, more than in any other mammal except some of the whales, dolphins and porpoises. The ears are prominent.*

*It used to be thought there were two species, the southeastern or rusty numbat and the banded numbat. These are now treated as one species, which originally ranged from western New South Wales across south and central Australia to Western Australia. In recent years the numbat has been seen in southwest Australia only and its range seems to be diminishing as human settlements spread.*

## Its food provides a home
Although sometimes lethargic, the numbat will suddenly run quickly in a series of bounds, and it will readily climb trees. Occasionally it will stand up on its hindlegs, straighten its back, and just take a look around. Normally its tail is carried straight out behind or with a slight upward curve. In moments of excitement the tail is curved upwards, or even over the back like a tree squirrel, and the hairs on it are fluffed out like a bottle-brush. Its home is in open woodland where the eucalyptus, known as the wandoo, sheds its branches which are soon hollowed out by termites. The numbat uses these for a shelter, taking in leaves and grass to form a nest. Numbats sleep soundly throughout the night in one of these hollow log shelters.

## Eats 7 million termites a year
The feeding habits of the numbat were first described by the Australian naturalist David Fleay, in 1952, 121 years after the animal was first discovered by a white man. He had one in captivity and offered it termites, several kinds of ants and their eggs, mealworms, beetles, insect grubs, earthworms, raw egg, bread and milk, honey and jam. It took only termites, swallowing the small ones whole, and chewing the larger species, and especially the soldier castes. It ate 10–20 thousand a day, picking them up by its cylindrical and extensible tongue which it flicked out rapidly in all directions to a length of 4 in. Only rarely did it eat ants, and these only when no termites were offered it. While feeding it flicked its tongue in and out of the termite galleries in the rotten wood, ignoring everything else. Any ants crawling over its legs were flicked off. JH Calaby has since made a study of the numbat's diet and has found that ants make up only 15% of the total and these are ants that have invaded termite colonies. While searching for termites the numbat uses its long snout as a probe or

# Nuthatch

*There are 31 species in the nuthatch family of which 18 are called true nut-hatches. They are small birds 4–7½ in. long with compact bodies, short tails, long, strong toes and claws and long tapering bills. Generally they are bluish-grey above and white, grey or chestnut on the under-parts, often with a black stripe through the eye. There are 15 nuthatches in the northern hemisphere, of which 4 are in North America. The 3 species in the southern hemisphere are blue-green above.*

*The commonest and most widely distributed species is the European nuthatch which ranges across much of Europe and Asia except for the extreme north. It is [5]½ in. long, slate-grey on the upperparts, and buff underneath with chestnut-red flanks. There is a conspicuous black stripe through the eye and the cheeks and throat are white. The tail is stumpy, black at the [ti]p and with white markings on the outer feathers.*

*The nuthatch lives in woods, parkland and large gardens with old broad-leaved trees. In Europe it is rarely seen in pinewoods but in eastern Asia it may live in dry pine forests high up the mountains.*

### Leaping up or down
The nuthatch leaps in short jerks over the trunks and branches of trees, upwards, downwards or sideways with equal ease, only holding on with its clawed toes as it does not use its tail as a support. Woodpeckers and tree-creepers cling with both feet together and use the tail as a prop. When a nuthatch rests it clings with one foot and props itself with the other. It is just as often seen coming down a tree-trunk headfirst as tailfirst, and when it goes to roost, in a depression or a crevice in the bark, it settles itself head downwards. Although not easy to see it is a noisy bird, which advertises its presence by a loud, frequently repeated, metallic call *chwit-chwit*.

### Nuts mainly in autumn
The name of this bird was originally nut-hack and in autumn its main food is hazel nuts. It places these in crevices in the bark low down on the trunks of mature trees such as oaks. Then it hammers the nut with its beak, swinging its body with each blow, like a woodman swinging an axe. The half shells usually remain fixed in the bark or fall to the base of the tree. Beechmasts, acorns, the seeds of yew and similar seeds are also opened and the kernels eaten. Nuthatches search the crevices of bark at other times for insects, including beetles, earwigs, flies and bugs, and galls are opened to extract the grubs. Spiders and small snails are

also eaten. With the increasing habit of putting bird tables in gardens, nuthatches have tended more and more to come near houses, to take bread and fat which they often wedge in crevices in trees. There is at least one record of a nuthatch actually burying a nut, pushing it deep down between the grass and the base of a tree with hard thrusts of the bill, then covering the hiding place with grass.

### Plastering the porch
In May the pair breed, choosing a cavity in the trunk of a tree or a stout branch, or sometimes a hole in a wall or in a nesting box. The entrance is made smaller by the nuthatches plastering mud around the opening, which sets hard. The cavity chosen may be an old woodpecker nest or a natural rot-cavity. Sometimes a sand martin's hole is used. The nest inside is made of dead leaves, bits of bark or grass, both partners sharing the work. The eggs, white and usually spotted with brown and streaked with violet, may number 6–11, with occasionally only 4–5. Incubation, which begins after the last egg is laid, is by the female only and it lasts about 14 days. The young are fed by both parents on small insects at first, later on caterpillars and spiders.

### Accident-prone babies?
There is little information about the enemies of nuthatches but because the number of

△ *Emerging from its bed the numbat takes a bleary-eyed look at the world around. It sleeps in a hollow log with its back to the entrance.*

else nips open termite infested wood or colonies in the earth, with its sharp claws.

### Cradle without a bottom
Although it is a marsupial a numbat has no pouch. The female, which is markedly smaller than the male, has four teats, surrounded by long crimped hairs. At first the babies merely cling to the teats with their mouths, but later they cling to the crimped hairs with their forefeet. When they have grown to a certain size the mother digs a hole in the ground, in which she leaves them while she goes foraging.

### Its backside is its safeguard
There seems some doubt about the enemies of the numbat. Twenty years ago there were fears that it might be on the road to extinction, due, so it was said, to the animal being killed by introduced foxes and domestic cats and dogs. Later researches suggest that it was the clearing of land, and especially the bush fires, that constituted the greatest danger. Once inside a log, and asleep, the numbat refuses to budge. This is its natural reaction because of the way it

tucks itself in. It points its head towards the closed end, tucks its tail under its body and closes the entrance with its broad rump. Vincent Serventy has described this as made up of solid muscle and feeling like wood when struck. It can also swell its body so it fits into the hollow like a cork. This is a trick used by a number of animals and has been called phragmoticism. The two possible enemies, a python known as the carpet snake, and the giant monitor lizard known as a goanna, cannot get a hold of an entrenched numbat. They must catch it in the open—perhaps surprising it while it is concentrating on termites—and even there its reaction to danger is to run rapidly to the nearest hollow log.

## Future in the balance
Studies made in the course of the last 20 years suggest that the numbat is more numerous than it was thought to be and that, as a species, it is no longer on the danger list. Even so, as human settlement spreads, there must come a time when the earlier fears will be revived. The wandoo yields a

very hard wood excellent for making charcoal. Its leaves also yield an essential oil valuable in industry. The numbat is in a family on its own, the last of its line. It is also a very unusual animal and relatively little is known about its way of life. It is wholly inoffensive and although it may make protesting noises—churring noises, like heavy breathing, and tut-tut-tut sounds—it has never been known to bite or show fight. Finally, in a land where termites are numerous a termite-eater has a decided value. There seems to be every argument therefore in favour of establishing a national park in the wandoo forest of south-west Australia and of supporting the efforts of those recommending as much protection as possible for the numbat.

| class | **Mammalia** |
|---|---|
| order | **Marsupialia** |
| family | **Myrmecobiidae** |
| genus & species | *Myrmecobius fasciatus* |

△ *Ready to crack. A European nutcracker is named for the way it cracks nuts and seeds.*

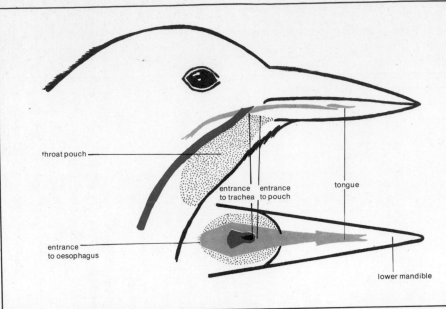

▽ *Cold snowy scene—a Clark's nutcracker stands on its prospective meal.*

△ *The nutcracker uses its throat pouch to carry food. The entrance is below the tongue.*

throat pouch

entrance
to trachea

entrance
to pouch

tongue

entrance
to oesophagus

lower mandible

A Plucinski

Russ Kinne·Photo Res

# Nutcracker

*The two species of nutcracker are unusual members of the crow family. About 1 ft long, the European nutcracker is dark brown with white flecks. When flying it is seen to have broad wings, a short tail and a noticeably long, pointed bill.*

*It ranges across central and northern Europe, but in European Russia and northern and central Asia is a subspecies, the slender-billed nutcracker. Clark's nutcracker, in western North America, much the same in habits, is largely grey with black and white wings and tail. The thick-billed and slender-billed subspecies are hard to tell apart in the field. The latter sometimes spreads into Europe coming as far west as the British Isles.*

### Jay-like in habits

Nutcrackers are at home in pine forests, or mixed woodlands in which conifers are plentiful. Outside the breeding season they disperse more into deciduous woods, especially where there is hazel. Then they move about in loose parties, spending much time on the ground, hopping heavily like jays. They also fly over the tops of tall trees or perch on their highest twigs, being less shy than jays. Their calls are harsh but less strident than those of jays and have a greater carrying power, and in spring they have a not unmusical babbling but they are always silent in the nesting season.

### Basic diet of pine seeds

This bird has acquired its name with reason. Inside the nutcracker's bill is a projection in the lower part which fits into a cavity in the upper part. Together they form highly efficient nutcrackers. Its food is largely the seeds from pine, spruce, cedar and larch cones and the Cembran or Arolla pine, also called the Swiss stone pine *Pinus cembra*, particularly favoured for its large wingless seeds. The seeds are usually picked out from the cones while they are hanging on the tree but nutcrackers may hold the cones with their feet while sitting on a branch or on the ground. This is especially true of the Arolla pine. Acorns, beechmast, hazel nuts and walnuts are also eaten as well as juniper berries. Insects and earthworms are taken as are the eggs and young of small woodland birds. Conifers supply the basic foods, however, and this determines the distribution and breeding range of the nutcrackers; and as the crop of seeds varies from year to year, so this influences the movements of the nutcrackers.

### Young fed on hazel nuts

The nest is always in a conifer, 15–30 ft from the ground, usually near the trunk. It is made of twigs, moss and lichens, reinforced with earth and lined with grass and the hairy lichen *Usnea barbata*. Usually 3 eggs are laid, bluish-green with olive-brown or grey markings, during March and April. These are incubated for 18 days, by the hen who is fed by her mate. The young remain in the nest for 3–4 weeks, during which time both parents feed them with food

Pamela Harrison

△ *Strange surroundings, for the European nutcracker is usually found in pine forests.*

brought to the nest in their throat pouches. The food is hazel nuts buried the previous autumn, the nutcrackers being able to find their hoards even when the ground is covered with snow (see jay p 1190). The success or otherwise of their breeding is directly linked with the hazel crop. When this is good as many as 4 or 5 eggs will be laid and there will be more young birds surviving the winter to breed next year.

### Migrations and eruptions

The areas in which thick-billed nutcrackers breed in central and northern Europe are limited largely to the mountains of Switzerland, the Carpathians and Balkans, and to southern Scandinavia. The slender-billed nutcrackers, less tied to mountain forests, extend from the forests of Baltic USSR across Siberia to Korea and Japan. There is, however, an isolated breeding area in Formosa and a more extensive zone through—

the foothills of the Himalayas and into southern China.

Clark's nutcracker of North America has a similar diet to that of the Eurasian nutcrackers although the species of pine it feeds on are different. There are, however, similar fluctuations in the crop of seeds so in poor years, the nutcrackers move down in the autumn and winter to lower altitudes to coastal and desert regions. Since 189[ ] there have been spectacular eruptions of thi[ ] kind in 1898-9, 1919-20, 1935-6, 1950-1 an[ ] 1955-6. These figures alone show that, [ ] is true also of the Eurasian nutcracke[ ] there are no regular cycles of eruption.

## Nuts, pigs and fur marke[ ]

It has been known for a long time that [ ] numbers of nutcrackers vary considera[ ] over the years and that from time to t[ ] they swarm westwards. For centuries [ ] arrival of nutcrackers in the autumn [ ] been feared by the people of the Ukra[ ] Poland and Germany as portents of disa[ ]

Peace of mind was restored when [ ] Russian AN Formosov showed, in 193[ ] remarkable links between the nutcra[ ] and the seeds of the Arolla pine, an[ ] supply of furs to the Siberian markets [ ] crackers hoard the seeds by pushing [ ] into the ground or into rocky cr[ ] There they germinate far more succe[ ] than do the seeds that fall naturall[ ] the cones and lie on top of the groun[ ] birds are, therefore, planting for [ ] generations as well as extending the [ ] for the species as a whole. It goes [ ] than this, however, because the Arol[ ] are a nutritious food for wild boa[ ] bear and squirrels. The crop of see[ ] a great deal. A bumper year may be [ ] by several mediocre or poor yea[ ] sometimes by a total failure of the [ ] the crop of seeds varies so do the [ ] of the squirrels, and this is reflect[ ] numbers of pelts reaching the [ ] markets. The numbers of nutcra[ ] varies, because it is when there [ ] Arolla crop that nutcrackers mus[ ] seek new feeding grounds by flyi[ ]

| class | **Aves** |
|---|---|
| order | **Passeriformes** |
| family | **Corvidae** |
| genus & species | ***Nucifraga caryocatact[ ]*** *Europe and Asia* ***N. columbianus*** *North [ ] or Clark's nutcracker* |

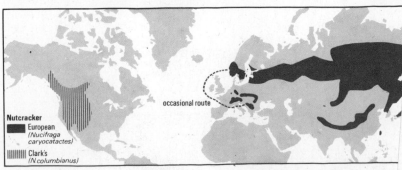

**Nutcracker**
**European**
*(Nucifraga caryocatactes)*

**Clark's**
*(N.columbianus)*

occasional route

eggs in a clutch is high it follows there must be a high death rate. These birds are no more vulnerable to birds of prey or ground predators than other small birds, and their nests must provide greater protection than most. There are indications that the small opening to the nest may constitute a danger to the young birds when making their first exit, in the form of broken legs and damaged wings. If true, this could mean there is an unusually high death rate among these young birds.

## Canada-Corsica axis

In North America there is the redbreasted nuthatch *Sitta canadensis*. It is unusual in having a white stripe above the black eyestripe. This species extends across southern Canada and southwards into the western United States and also into the New England states in the east. Across the Pacific, thousands of miles from the west coast of America, is another nuthatch living in Korea and also in a wide arc through central China. A bird very like it lives in Turkey and the Caucasus. Then comes the biggest surprise of all: a bird to all appearances indistinguishable from the redbreasted nuthatch in North America, eastern Asia and Asia Minor lives on the island of Corsica and nowhere else in Europe. Leading ornithologists having made a close study of nuthatches from these various areas, have

come to the conclusion that either they all belong to one species or to four species that nobody can tell apart. If they all belong to one species then the puzzle is why they should occur over such widely separated areas. And there is another puzzle: why should one species live on the island of Corsica and not on Sardinia or in Italy or southern France?

| class | **Aves** |
|---|---|
| order | **Passeriformes** |
| family | **Sittidae** |
| genus & species | ***Sitta canadensis*** *N. American red-breasted nuthatch* ***S. europaea*** *others* |

*All set for landing — white breasted nuthatch,* **Sitta carolinensis** *(opposite page). This common, fearless bird lives in North America from southern Canada to northern Mexico. Throughout its range it nests in hollows in trees or stumps, even in nest boxes. Upwards or downwards, the nuthatch is well known for its habit of walking in all directions on the trunks and branches of trees. Unlike woodpeckers and creepers the nuthatch never uses its tail as a brace but climbs along tree trunks by clinging with its long, strong toes and talons, as the picture of the white breasted species (above left) shows. Efficient nutcracker: European nuthatch (above right). The nuthatch gets its name from the way it wedges nuts between cracks in the bark of trees and then proceeds to crack them open with hammerlike blows from its 'hatchet' bill.*

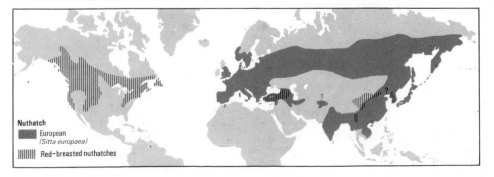

Nuthatch

Red-breasted nuthatches

European *(Sitta europaea)*

# Nutshell

*Although insignificant compared with some of the larger, more colourful marine shells, nutshells are interesting because of their peculiar ways of feeding and moving about. They are also very numerous.*

*The nutshell is a primitive bivalve mollusc shaped like a hazel nut, rounded but nearly triangular in outline. The many species, which all look much alike, are found in all temperate and tropical seas, from 9 ft down to 600 ft. They are mainly small, usually about ½ in. long, exceptionally ¾ in., yellow, olive or grey, sometimes with red-brown or purple-grey rays radiating from the hinge region. The colour is mainly in the outer protein layer, but this may wear off empty shells. At the apex of the shell is the hinge and the dark brown elastic ligament that pushes the shell open. On either side of this each valve has a row of teeth which interlock and help to keep the valves aligned. The edge of each valve is notched, except in the species known as the thin nutshell.*

## The muddy life

Nutshells can be extremely common—so much so that in some areas they are the most abundant of the invertebrates apart from those of near-microscopic size. Nutshells live on the seabed, wherever they can bury themselves, each species thriving best on deposits of a particular degree of coarseness, from mud to sandy gravel. They burrow with a muscular foot that is unlike that of most other bivalves in that it ends in a sole folded down the middle and with the two halves facing outwards. The foot is thrust out from between the valves and the two halves are opened at the tip to grip the seabed. The rest of the foot then contracts and draws the body along. As a rule, however, nutshells do not move about much, they may stay in the same position for several days.

There is really little need for them to move since their food is made up of small organic particles in the sand or mud with which the animal is normally just covered, hinge uppermost. A current of water for respiration, containing minute food particles of mainly dead animal and plant matter, is drawn in at the front of the shell by beating cilia, then driven out at the rear. Sometimes when too much debris accumulates, the valves will suddenly close. This drives a strong current across the gills to clean them. There are no siphons such as there are in many bivalves for carrying the ingoing and outgoing currents.

## They probe for food

Most bivalves feed by filtering small particles from the water, using their large, complex gills. The particles are passed for sorting to smaller ciliated flaps called palps which direct only the most suitable ones to the nearby mouth. This method of feeding is only part of the story for nutshells. Their gills are small and simple, the palps are large and complex and they have something not

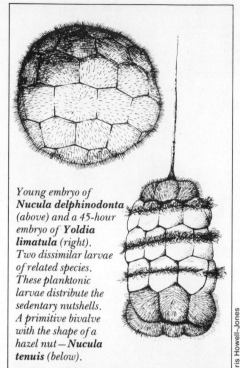

*Young embryo of **Nucula delphinodonta** (above) and a 45-hour embryo of **Yoldia limatula** (right). Two dissimilar larvae of related species. These planktonic larvae distribute the sedentary nutshells. A primitive bivalve with the shape of a hazel nut—**Nucula tenuis** (below).*

Chris Howell-Jones

Natural History Museum

found in other bivalves: a pair of long 'palp-proboscides'. At the front end of each palp is a proboscis long enough to be pushed some way out of the shell. It is very muscular, contractile and active. Along one side is a groove lined with cilia and as the proboscis feels around in the sand or mud, small organic particles are picked up and carried along the groove to the main part of the palp via a flap-like structure called the palp pouch.

There is a palp on either side of the foot and each is made up of two large flaps, or lamellae. The out-turned faces of these flaps are covered with ciliated ridges and it is on these that the particles are sorted. As well as the particles brought in by the palp-proboscides, there are the others carried in with the water current. Some of these are caught on the outer surfaces of the palps and more are passed from the gills to the palps in the same way as in other bivalves. Not all the particles trapped by the gills go to the palps because a good deal of sorting goes on. The heaviest sediment is trapped on the lower surfaces of the gills and carried by cilia to the edge of the mantle tissue

lining the shell and thrown out. The particles rejected by the palps leave at the same place. Very fine particles pass through the gills, are trapped in a slime from glands on the other side, then rejected.

## Strange carrycot

The breeding season varies from species to species. Eggs, about $\frac{1}{250}$ in. across, and sperms, are shed into the sea through the kidneys. After fertilisation, the egg develops into a larva that swims by the beating of three belts of cilia round its barrel-shaped body. There is also a patch of cilia at each end and a tuft of very long cilia at the apex. Eventually, the outer layer of cells of this larva are cast off to reveal a young bivalve complete with tiny shell. This is probably the typical sequence in the development but there are some interesting departures from it in an American species *Nucula delphinodonta*. In this the larvae are kept for three or four weeks in a brood sac of mucus-like material mixed with foreign bodies that is attached to the hind end of the shell. With this protection of the young and the increased chances of their survival, only 20–70 eggs are laid, but they are larger than usual, about $\frac{1}{120}$ in. across. It is neither necessary nor useful for the larvae in the brood sac to swim around very actively so in this species the cilia are distributed evenly instead of in belts, a less efficient arrangement for movement. Here we have a good example of the differences in structures between larvae of closely related species reflecting different ways of life. Another point which it illustrates is the general principle that a species has the 'choice' of producing many, perhaps millions, of eggs, each with a slender chance of survival, or of producing just a few that are well nourished and protected.

# Oldfashioned shells

Nutshells are one of the most primitive of bivalves. Their immediate ancestors lived nearly 500 million years ago, while nutshells not unlike those living today were on the earth nearly 400 million years ago. If they were not so numerous we should speak of them as living fossils. As it is they are all over the place. Their empty shells are cast up by storms onto the beaches. One species, the thin nutshell, lives off all the coasts of the northern hemisphere, and another ranges from Norway down to the Cape and round to Natal in the Indian Ocean. So nutshells have survived, even with outmoded tools, for their method of feeding is clumsy and complex, and most bivalves have abandoned it in favour of large gills, which are more efficient, not only for breathing but for drawing in particles of food. Nevertheless, outmoded or not, the method used by nutshells works and it has done so for 400 million years.

| phylum | **Mollusca** |
|--------|--------------|
| class | **Bivalvia** |
| order | **Protobranchia** |
| family | **Nuculidae** |
| genus & species | ***Nucula sulcata*** furrowed nutshell ***N. tenuis*** thin nutshell, others |

# Nyala

The nyala and its two relatives form a group of ox-like antelopes which includes the bushbuck (p 325) and the kudu (p 1262). They all have white spots and stripes on the body and throat fringes, and the males have twisted horns with yellow tips. The true nyala or inyala, which stands 42 in. high and weighs 250–275 lb, is a very beautiful antelope, and by far the most striking of the three. The male, quite different in appearance from the female, is slate grey with a red forehead and has a long fringe of hair on the throat and underparts. His upper lip, chin, ear-bases and two cheek-spots are white and he has a white stripe across the nose. There is a white chest-band, and about 14 white body-stripes. A few haunch-spots, the dorsal crest and the underside of the tail, are also white. The legs, from just above the knees and hocks to the hoofs, are bright tan, with a white patch on the inner sides of the knees and hocks. The female is bright chestnut with a dark nose, white face-band, about 11 body-stripes and fewer white haunch-spots. Her dorsal crest is shorter than the male's and is only white where the stripes cross it, and she has no throat fringe. The mountain nyala is 52 in. high and weighs 450–500 lb. It has a longer, coarser coat and a shorter throat fringe. It is brown-grey with a short dark mane, and has no body-stripes, but it has a characteristic line of 9 spots along the haunches. In addition to the face-marks and chest-patch, there is a crescent on the throat, and the inner sides of the forelegs are white. The third species is the sitatunga or marshbuck, which is 32–42 in. high, has a long, coarse grey-brown to red-brown coat with a heavy fringe on the throat and underparts. It has the same markings as in the true nyala as well as a throat-crescent. It has long hoofs, 3 in. long, and the backs of the pasterns, which are bare, supple and rubbery, are adapted to walking on soft marshy ground.

Nyala occur in northeastern Natal, Eastern Transvaal, Rhodesia and southern Malawi. Because of their strict habitat requirements, sitatunga live in three separate areas: the Niger river and Lake Chad, west as far as Gambia; the Congo-Zambesi headwaters region, as far as the Ngami and Okovango swamps in Botswana; and Lake Victoria and the White Nile. They have populated several of the islands in Lake Victoria, including the rather dry, desolate Nkosi islands. A special race with short, firm hooves and the solid foot structure of the nyala, has adapted to this terrain in which the supple feet and spreading hoofs of the other sitatunga would be a disadvantage.

## Keeping well hidden

As the habitat of the nyala seems to have been disturbed by man for a long time, the presence of these shy, secretive creatures was not suspected until fairly recently. Now, however, they have got used to tourists in the National Parks and come more into the open. They usually live in lush green river country where they feed on grass, leaves and fallen fruit. The rams live singly or in small groups; the females and young form separate herds of 8–16, which commonly associate with impala herds where they are often unnoticed as, except for the stripes, they are much the same colour. They constantly wag their tails from side to side as they move about. Like kudus, nyala have hairy glands on their hindfeet, which leave their scent where they walk. Mountain nyala and sitatunga do not have these. When a male nyala displays, he raises his white dorsal crest, lowers his horns and moves stiffly, as when entering the females' herds during the rut.

Sitatunga spend the day in papyrus swamps, entering water up to 4 ft deep. At night they come out onto the marshlands to feed. When they are feeding in water, they often submerge completely and they are said to escape from predators by hiding under the water with just the nose above the surface. Like nyala they are rarely seen, so are often thought to be scarcer than they are.

▽ A striking male nyala drinks a short distance from a striped doe and a pair of impalas.

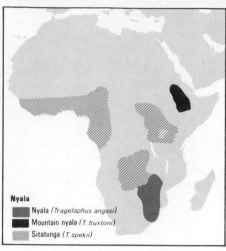

**Nyala**
- ■ Nyala (*Tragelaphus angasi*)
- ■ Mountain nyala (*T. buxtoni*)
- ▨ Sitatunga (*T. spekii*)

*Nyala usually live near rivers in lush green grasslands or forests. The sitatunga is restricted to swamps and marshes.*

### Breeding not studied

Little is known about the breeding habits of nyala and sitatunga. In the nyala gestation is thought to be about 6 months, and a single young is born usually in September or Octo-ber. The young lie hidden in grass until they are old enough to move around with the rest of the herd. The gestation of the sitatunga is nearer 8 months.

### A difficult meal

Nyalas are preyed upon by leopards, and sometimes by lions and cape hunting dogs. Although normally peaceful, the rams become very fierce when attacked. The sitatunga's habit of taking refuge in deep water, effective against natural enemies, has proved a disadvantage against man. African hunters paddle out to the hiding antelope, identify it by its nose breaking the surface, and spear it.

## Mountain refuge

The largest of the three species is the splendid mountain nyala of Ethiopia, the size of a greater kudu. It is not as colourful or as beautiful as its South African relative, the nyala, but it is rarer and more unusual. Its horns form a much more open spiral, are less twisted than the sitatunga's, having only 1¼ turns instead of 2. The mountain nyala seems to be yet another species that has found refuge in the mountains. It lives high up in the mountains of the Ethiopian plateau, in the high moorlands among the giant heaths *Erica arborea* and St John's wort *Hypericum lanceolatum* east of the Rift valley, at 9 500 – 12 500 ft or even higher from Mount Gugu southwest to the Chilalo and Kaka ranges and the Bale Mountains. It seems to be doing well, at least for the moment. In 1963, LH Brown reported that its numbers were low, perhaps only about 2 000 in all, but that it was not in immediate danger of extinction. In 1967 he revised his estimate, to 4–5 thousand. Even so, we know little more about its way of life than that the young are born in June and July, at the height of summer. For more knowledge about it we may have to wait until somebody goes and lives for several years high up in the mountains, as Jane Goodall and others have lived with the apes.

| class | **Mammalia** |
|---|---|
| order | **Artiodactyla** |
| family | **Bovidae** |
| genus & species | ***Tragelaphus angasi*** *nyala* <br> ***T. buxtoni*** *mountain nyala* <br> ***T. spekii*** *sitatunga* |

▽ *A chestnut-coloured female nyala occupies the limelight while her young lies quietly on the grass behind. Nyala are extremely shy by nature, so much so that their existence remained unsuspected for a long time, especially as they haunt impenetrable and fever-infested areas.*

SEF

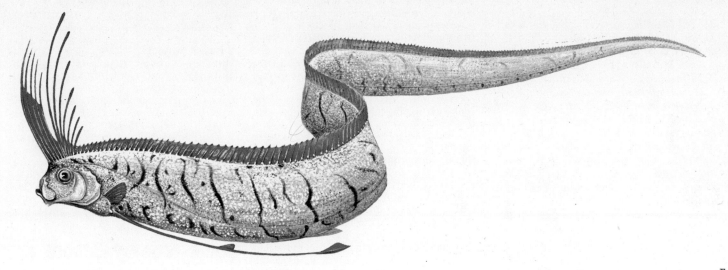

John Norris Wood

*An oarfish with its oars, the pelvic fins, trailing at its side, and its crest, the first 10 rays of the continuous dorsal fin, raised in an aggressive pose.*

# Oarfish

*This has been described as one of the most mysterious of the larger sea fishes, and has often been linked with stories of sea-serpents. Its real interest, however, lies in its extraordinary shape, its large size and how little we know of its way of life. There is only one species, but oarfishes large and small have been found floating on the surface or washed ashore in warm and temperate seas throughout the world.*

*Sometimes called the ribbonfish, the oarfish has a flattened body up to 1 ft deep and only 2 in. across; it is up to 20 ft or more long. Hard knobs stud the skin, which is silvery with a bluish tinge on the head and is marked with dark streaks, sometimes with dark spots. The eyes are large. The fins are coral red. The dorsal fin starts on top of the head between the eyes and runs all the way to the hindend of the body. Because the first 10—12 rays of this are long, it makes a spectacular mane or crest over the head. People who have had first hand encounters with living oarfishes report that when the fish is touched it raises this 'mane', almost as if it were an aggressive display. The tail fin is very small or missing altogether. The pectoral fins are small but the pelvic fins, lying just under them, are long and slender, broadening at their tips, like oars.*

## An elusive king

Varying opinions put the oarfish's home anywhere between the surface and 3 000 ft deep. It is generally believed, however, that when an oarfish is seen at the surface it is sick or dying. A report of an oarfish swimming towards the *Florida,* in 1958, pursued by a shark, suggests that not all oarfishes seen at the surface are weak or moribund. Moreover, the oarfish has been called the King of the Herrings because it was once believed that it swam in front of the herring shoals, as if leading them. This must mean they were not unfamiliar to fishermen. No adult oarfish has ever been caught in a net, however, possibly because of the speed at which it can slip through the water with wave-like movements of the long thin body.

## Washed ashore

Oarfish are rarely reported; only 16 were captured in British waters from 1759 to 1878, according to Dr Albert Gunther, and since then they have been caught about once every 10 years. Sir Alister Hardy thinks that oarfishes have 'been taken as often in our waters as anywhere else in the world, except perhaps off Japan'. Nevertheless, in the newspapers and magazines, as well as in the scientific journals of the world, there are a number of records of oarfishes, from 2 ft long to 20 ft or more, being captured or washed ashore, and there must be many more seen but not captured. So wherever it lives, this unusually shaped fish comes close enough to land to be familiar to sailors and fishermen everywhere.

## Large fish, small food

An oarfish has a very small mouth and no teeth. It has a large number of long spiny gill-rakers, the number varying from 42 to 58. These strain very small crustaceans, especially those known as euphausids, from the water passing over the gills.

## Baby bunting

The larvae, which hatch from small, floating eggs, have remarkable streamers, ornamented with small tags of skin. These streamers are made up of the much elongated rays of the front part of the dorsal fin and of the similarly elongated pelvic fins. What purpose they serve is unknown.

## Glutton for punishment

Except for the shark seen chasing an oarfish there is no direct evidence about its enemies. A high percentage of captured oarfishes, however, have either lost a part of the tail or have scars from old wounds somewhere on the rear half of the body. It seems that an oarfish can lose nearly half its body yet still survive. The internal organs are all packed into the front quarter of the body, although there is a large bag connected with the stomach, an accessory digestive organ, which extends back among the muscles of the tail to about the centre of the body. Therefore —or so it seems from studying the captured specimens—an oarfish can survive provided only the rear half is bitten, even if it is bitten off completely.

# Regal coincidence

Related to the oarfishes are the dealfishes, family Trachipteridae. These have a similar shape to the oarfishes but are shorter and higher in the body. They also lack the 'mane' and have only small pelvic fins. They have a small fan-shaped tail fin which points obliquely upwards. Dealfish grow to 8 ft long and there are a number of species. *Trachypterus arcticus* lives in the North Atlantic, *T. iris* is in the Mediterranean, and there is one which is sometimes seen off the Pacific coast of North America, where the big runs of salmon occur. This is named *T. rex-salmonorum* because the North American Indians living on the coast there had similar beliefs to the herring fishermen of Europe. They believed that the dealfish led the salmon, so they misleadingly called it the King of the Salmon.

| class | **Pisces** |
|---|---|
| order | **Lampridiformes** |
| family | **Regalecidae** |
| genus & species | ***Regalecus glesne*** |

# Ocean sunfish

*Shaped like a millstone—its scientific name* **Mola** *is Latin for millstone—this fish has been described as weighing a ton although it has a spinal cord only ½ in. long, which is, in fact, shorter than the brain.*

*It looks all head, and these fishes are sometimes called headfishes. Its body is oval and covered with a thick leathery skin, grey, olive-brown or nearly black with silvery reflections. The snout projects beyond the small mouth in which the teeth in both upper and lower jaws are joined to form a single sharp-edged beak. The dorsal and anal fins are large and high and the body ends abruptly in a low tail fin. In the ocean sunfish* **Mola mola** *the tail is rounded and wavy, but it is slightly different in the two related species. In the pointed-tailed sunfish* **M. lanceolata** *it is drawn out into a point in the middle, and in the oblong or truncated sunfish* **Ranzania truncata** *it has a rounded margin. The first of these species is up to 10 ft long and weighs a ton or more. The other two are smaller, the third seldom exceeding 2 ft long. All three are found in the warmer seas and occasionally in temperate seas, throughout the world.*

## Novel navigation

Ocean sunfish will sometimes lie at the surface somewhat obliquely with the dorsal fin above the surface, as if basking in the sun, or so the stories have always said. Doubts were raised about this during the last quarter of a century when people began to think that when ocean sunfishes are seen on the surface they must be either dead or dying. Several times these fishes have been seen well up rivers, as if carried in helplessly on the tide, and in Monterey Bay, in California, in October 1960, there was a very heavy death rate among ocean sunfishes close inshore. Skindivers went down and saw a hundred of them in 50 ft of water and all had their fins bitten off and most of them had lost their eyes. On the same day a little away from that

spot a score or more were seen floating on the surface and in these also the fins and eyes had been damaged. The cause of death is unknown but Daniel W Gotshall, who investigated this event, concluded that when sunfishes are seen floating at or near the surface the chances are they are sick or dying, not that they have come to the surface to bask in the sun.

Underwater observations made by the Italian, L Roghi, seem to bear this out. He tells us how, when the sunfish is at rest, it lies stationary in the water with its tail down and its mouth pointing upwards. While in this position it goes a darker colour except for the fins and a large area around the throat. He then describes how, as soon as the fish starts to swim, it immediately, and very strikingly, changes to a very light colour. If sunfishes came to the surface to bask we should expect, from what Roghi tells us, that they would be light in colour and would rest nose up. A few years ago two Dutch zoologists who listed the 57 records of ocean sunfishes taken off the coast of Holland during the years 1836–1959 showed that the great majority were caught in the months of November and December. No healthy warm-water fish would allow itself to drift north in winter.

Although often at or near the surface, especially in calm weather, ocean sunfish may possibly go down to depths of 600 ft at times. The ocean sunfish is usually seen singly or in pairs but it may come together in schools of a dozen or more at certain times of the year.

## Steering by jets

Ocean sunfish wave both dorsal and anal fins in unison from side to side, in a sculling action, the fins twisting slightly as they wave. The small pectoral fins flap continually but they probably act only as stabilizers. The tail is used as a rudder, while the sunfish steers with its gills by squirting a strong jet of water out of one gill-opening or the other, or out of its mouth. Sunfishes have no need for speed because their food is mainly plankton and includes jellyfishes, planktonic molluscs, small crustaceans and fish larvae. Leading this kind of life it does not need much intelligence, and not only is its spinal

cord short, its brain is very small. In fact, the brain is smaller than either of the two kidneys that lie just behind it, instead of farther back in the body, as is usual.

## Normal infancy

Although so like a caricature of a fish when adult, the baby ocean sunfish is a normal shape. From dissection of captured sunfish it is estimated that the female's ovary may contain 300 million eggs. The larvae are about 1/10 in. long and almost the usual shape of a fish. This soon changes as the dorsal and anal fins begin to grow and the body becomes covered with spines. Then this coat of spines is lost until only 5 long spines are left. These then shorten until they are lost completely, and the bulky, disc-shaped body begins to take form. The baby fish is then about ½ in. long.

## Bullet-proof waistcoat

In the past people have tried to harpoon or shoot sunfishes, but they have had the greatest difficulty in doing so. The sunfish made no attempt to escape by diving, or by swimming away as they could not go any faster than a rowing boat. All they did was to make sounds like pigs grunting, or else they just sighed. One was described as making hideous groans. These sounds, which are made by grinding their throat teeth, may or may not indicate distress, but the reason the sunfish takes no evasive action probably lies in the 2–3 in. coat of gristle under its tough skin. Even expert harpooners have had to try a dozen times before piercing this tough coat, and one sunfish lying off the coast of New South Wales, Australia, was proof against bullets. Its 'tough hide rendered it impervious to bullets fired from Winchester rifles!' Presumably, therefore, ocean sunfishes have no enemies except when they are very small.

| class | **Pisces** |
|---|---|
| order | **Tetraodontiformes** |
| family | **Molidae** |
| genus & species | *Mola mola* |

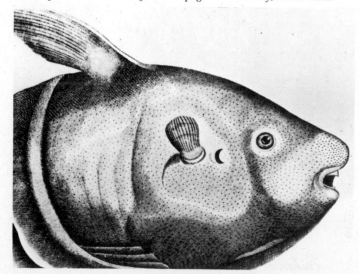

▽ *Fins folded back so as to fit on the page! 17th century,* **Mola mola**.

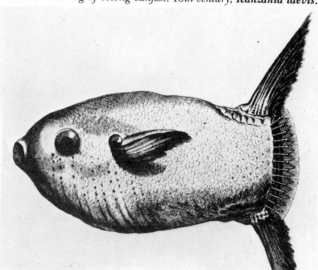

▽ *Artistic rendering of oblong sunfish. 18th century,* **Ranzania laevis**.

*Old print of ocean sunfish, **Mola mola**.*

# Spots . . . and spots

*Cheetah* **Acinonyx jubatus**. *Solid black spots, set close together, cover the tawny body.*

*Leopard* **Panthera pardus**. *A pattern of black spots mainly arranged in rosettes.*

*Jaguar* **Panthera onca**. *A similar pattern but with black spots in the centres of the rosettes.*

*Ocelot* **Felis pardalis**. *Marked with large brown, black-bordered spots and blotches.*

*Tiger* **Panthera tigris**. *The familiar dark, broken stripes ring its tawny coat.*

# Ocelot

*One of the most beautiful members of the cat family, the ocelot's short-haired coat varies considerably in colour. It may be from pale grey to greyish yellow or deep warm brown, blotched with large brown black-bordered spots and there are black streaks round the head and neck. It has very long legs and is medium sized, being up to 4 ft long, with a 15-in. tail, and weighing up to 35 lb. The name 'ocelot' is from a Mexican word tlalocelotl, meaning field-tiger. The pattern of its coat makes it very inconspicuous in its native forests and so helps it considerably when hunting. The margay cat, which is about the size of a domestic cat and is closely related to the ocelot, is bright cream-yellow in colour and spotted with jet black. It is up to 13 lb weight and has a very long tail.*

*Owing to their attractive appearance the ocelot and the margay are frequently taken when very young and reared by hand, especially in the United States and they make tame, affectionate pets. They become unpredictable and often dangerous, however, when they are adult.*

*The ocelot is found in the southwest United States, throughout Mexico and Central America and in South America from Paraguay northwards. The margay is found over most of this range but is less numerous than the ocelot.*

## Hunting in the thickets

A forest-loving animal, the ocelot generally keeps to dense cover. Although it can climb well it normally hunts on the forest floor, making good use of its acute hearing and sight. Unlike most cats, the ocelot swims well. It is mainly nocturnal and quite often hunts in pairs, both mewing continually to keep in touch with each other. It confines its hunting to a more or less fixed territory which it defends against its own kind. It marks this territory with its own scent by heaping up mounds of its excrement.

## Eats anything small enough

The ocelot will prey on almost any animal it can overpower; small mammals, including rats, mice, and agoutis, and monkeys, birds, reptiles and frogs. Although it eats mainly wild animals it is a danger to domestic stock and poultry, taking even lambs or pigs.

## Breeding mystery

There seems to be a difference of opinion about the breeding season. One writer says the mating takes place in June and July and another that it begins in December and January. Yet another asserts that there may be two litters a year, born at any time. Usually there are two in a litter, well-furred but blind. The nest is made of grass or other soft material in a hollow log, among rocks or under a bush.

## Dangerous beauty

Although the ocelot's coat makes it inconspicuous where it lives it has the disadvantage that it makes desirable fur coats and collars. The fur is expensive as no two ocelots have identical markings and fur dealers have great difficulty in matching up the pelts. In spite of being hunted, ocelots do not seem to be in danger of extinction because of their high reproductive rate and the type of country they inhabit.

## Cats and their prey

Most members of the cat family, including the domestic cat, stalk their prey. When it first sees a mouse or small mammal at some distance, a cat will crouch down, then slink quickly towards it with its body flat to the ground. When it gets near, the cat will pause and watch, with its whiskers spread out and ears pricked forwards. It then stalks its prey, moving forward slowly and cautiously and using any available cover until it launches its final attack. This is not usually a single leap but a short run with the body flat to the ground and then a final thrust forward with the forequarters to seize the prey while the hind feet are kept firmly planted on the ground to keep the cat balanced should a struggle follow.

This hunting behaviour may be seen even in the play of kittens and is an adaptation for catching small rodents, not for killing birds. In contrast with most members of the cat family, who are not clever at catching birds, the ocelot is adept at killing them. It makes a direct attack, not an ambush, the instant it sees a bird. Even when hunting mammals, the ocelot attacks directly.

Most cats, including the ocelot, kill their prey with a single bite at the nape of the neck. If the prey is long-necked the first bite is made in the shoulder region near the base of the neck and a second bite just behind the head. The ocelot uses this same method for killing birds.

The domestic cat always eats a mouse by starting at the head but the larger cats when dealing with prey too large for this method, usually start at the belly or groin. A margay which was seen eating a rabbit, made repeated efforts to start at the head and only bit elsewhere when it found it could not break the skull bones.

# Large-eyed retriever

The initial attractiveness of the margay as a pet springs to some extent from the large size of its eyes, which are unusually large even for a member of the cat family. After that, experiences differ on how far they are desirable as pets. There is, for example, the report of a margay cat, left alone in a Washington apartment with a small baby, eating the infant's toes. By contrast Mrs Si Merrill, writing in *Animals* for September 1963, has described how affectionate her pet margay was. Her account is illuminating for two other things. First, there was the margay's addiction to drinking coffee whenever it could. On one occasion, moreover, when it upset a cup of it on the floor it spent 10 minutes 'rolling in it, sliding about on its back and stomach, until its fur had absorbed it all'. This is very like the characteristic behaviour of felines with catmint, and it is interesting to find another substance that will, apparently, stimulate the same rather surprising behaviour.

The other feature of this particular margay was that it would not only play with a toy thrown to it but would bring it back for it to be thrown again. It would also carry a toy to a person to initiate the play. This kind of retrieving we usually associate with dogs rather than cats.

| class | **Mammalia** |
|---|---|
| order | **Carnivora** |
| family | **Felidae** |
| genus & species | ***Felis pardalis*** *ocelot* <br> ***F. wiedi*** *margay cat* |

▽ *Night prowler. The ocelot's coat makes it inconspicuous as it prowls through the forests.*

# Octopus

The name 'octopus' means literally 'eight feet' and the animal, indeed, has eight arms, joined at their bases by a web, and surrounding a beaked mouth. Octopuses differ most obviously from squids and cuttlefishes, the other well known members of the Cephalopoda, in lacking the extra pair of long tentacles. Moreover, their suckers, which run right along the arms, are not strengthened by the horny rings seen in the suckers of squids. Other differences are that octopuses have no trace of an internal shell and their body is short and rounded instead of being streamlined.

The 150 species of octopuses are distributed throughout the seas of the world, but are especially numerous in warm seas. The smallest is **Octopus arborescens,** less than 2 in. across. The largest is the Pacific octopus, **O. hongkongensis** which reaches 32 ft across the arms although its thimble-shaped body is only 18 in. long. Another giant is **O. apollyon,** of the North Pacific, 28 ft across. The Octopoda also include species that are very different in form. One is the argonaut (p 82). Another is the blind deep-sea **Cirrothauma** of the North Atlantic, which has two large fins on its body. The web between its arms reaches almost to their tips and it swims by opening and closing this umbrella. Besides the suckers on the undersides of its arms, it has rows of filaments which are believed to be used for catching food particles. Its body has the texture of a jelly-fish and it is said to be so transparent one can read newsprint through it. The common octopus, the species mainly dealt with here, lives off the coasts of tropical and subtropical Africa and Atlantic America, is especially numerous in the Mediterranean, and reaches the southern coasts of the British Isles. It may, exceptionally, reach a span of 10 ft but is usually much smaller. The lesser octopus, ranges from Norway to the Mediterranean. It is rarely more than 2½ ft across the widest span of its arms and can be readily recognized by the single row of suckers on its arms, instead of the double row in the common octopus.

## Master of disguise

The common octopus lives among rocks in shallow water, spending much of the time in a hole in the rocks or in a 'villa' built of stones. When outside, it creeps about on its arms most of the time, using its suckers to grip, though it can also swim. It usually swims backwards with its arms trailing, by blowing water out through its siphon. As in cuttlefish and squid, this water is blown out from the mantle cavity which houses the gills and the openings of the kidneys, rectum, reproductive organs and ink sac. Like cuttlefish and squid it can send out a cloud of ink to baffle pursuers.

There is no evidence that octopuses react to sound. However, the arms are very sensitive to touch and taste, and the eyes are well developed. The importance of vision is reflected in their outstanding ability to change colour. This is done with two kinds of chromatophores, or pigment cells, in the skin that vary in colour according to how much they are expanded or contracted. One kind varies from black to red-brown and the other from red to pale orange-yellow. Beneath these chromatophores is a layer of small bodies known as iridocytes that reflect white light or give a blue or green by refraction. The variation in appearance is not, however, just a matter of colour patterns but also of posture and of general texture. The arms may be extended, tucked underneath or curled stiffly back over the body as armour and the suckers may be out of sight or protruded to give the arms a wavy outline. By suitable adjustments in colour, posture and texture an octopus can merge completely with its background so it is extremely difficult to see. Octopuses also have a conspicuous display that often gives them away to fishermen searching for them. This is the so-called dymantic display, given when octopuses are frightened by large objects. The animal flattens out, coiling its arms in beside the body and extending the web between them. The body grows pale but dark rings develop around the eyes and the edge of the web also becomes dark. Presumably the purpose of this display is to deter predators, at least long enough for the octopus to change colour, blow ink and shoot away. With their large brains and adaptable behaviour, octopuses have been the object of a number of revealing studies on learning and brain function in lower animals. In captivity they rapidly settle down and become used to their captors.

## Octopus attack

An octopus usually attacks only moving objects. It glides smoothly to within a few inches of its prey, collects itself together and then jumps forwards at it with a sudden backwards spurt from the jet. Small prey, mainly fish and crustaceans, is trapped beneath the expanded web between the arms, and then seized with the parrot-like horny beak around its mouth. At the same time a poison is given out that paralyses the prey. An average-sized octopus eats perhaps two dozen small crabs in a day. There are many reports of people being seized and held by octopuses and there is little doubt this does happen, perhaps rarely, and especially in warm seas. It seems, however, that these are not deliberate attacks but more a matter of investigating a moving object, and people have found that if they keep still, the octopuses will 'feel' them for a short while, then let go.

## Coldblooded courtship

In mating, which may take several hours, male and female sit apart. There is almost no courtship display, although the male may expose certain particularly large suckers near the base of the second pair of arms, as if 'making a pass' at the female. The only contact he has with her is through a single arm which he extends to caress her. This arm is always the third arm on the right side which is specially modified for the purpose and has a spoon-shaped tip. It is called the hectocotylus arm for reasons given in the article on the argonaut (p 82).

▽ Smoke screen: an octopus ejects a cloud of ink to deter a predator and to escape behind.

▷▽ Tiny suction pads to grip the rock cover the tentacles which surround a central mouth.

▷ A cruel but beautiful animal, an octopus glides effortlessly through the deeps.

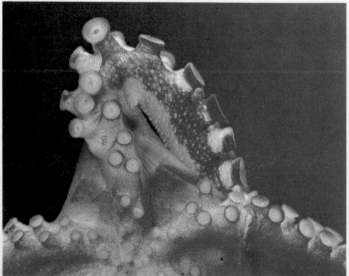

△ *Blue-ringed octopus* **Hapalochlaena maculosa** *swimming backwards, its arms trailing.*

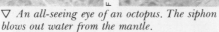

▽ *An all-seeing eye of an octopus. The siphon blows out water from the mantle.*

△ *Sea-spider: blue-ringed octopus. It usually attacks only moving objects.*

The tip is placed in the female's gill cavity and the sperms are deposited near the opening of her oviduct in elaborate packages called spermatophores.

A female lays about 150 000 eggs in about a week, each in an oval capsule slightly smaller than a grain of rice. They are attached by short stalks to long strands that festoon the mother's lair. The mother broods over the eggs for several weeks, often cleaning them with her arms or blowing water over them with her funnel. During this time, she eats little. Indeed, she may fast completely for weeks, or for as much as 4 months in one species, and a brooding female in an aquarium has been seen to remove food placed near her and drop it well away from her. The short-armed young hatch at about $\frac{1}{8}$ in. long and drift around for a while before they start their own life on the bottom, by which time they may be $\frac{1}{2}$ in. long and several weeks old. The common octopus rarely, if ever, breeds on the coasts of the British Isles although, year after year, larvae migrate across the Channel from Brittany. Sometimes after a mild winter, the numbers of octopus may reach plague proportions, to the detriment of the crabs and lobsters.

## True or not true?

It is sometimes said that octopuses can feed on bivalve shellfish by jamming stones

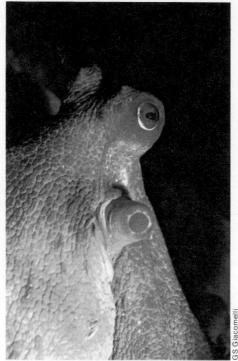

between the valves to stop them closing. Pliny, the Roman naturalist, recorded this and in 1857 Jeannette Power, the French naturalist, wrote of an octopus, failing to force open a large mussel, picking up a stone and inserting it when the shell next opened. This is a pretty tale and not to be discounted out of hand, but several zoologists have watched in vain for this behaviour, and some have experimented with octopuses in aquaria but without result. Moreover, it is unlikely that the octopus, for all its relatively capable brain and sensitive arms, can ever perform such skilled manipulations. The trouble is that the shape of the body is just too variable, so the nervous system would need to be very complex to take into account all the bends and twists in the arms, and at the same time monitor and control such an intelligent action.

| phylum | **Mollusca** |
|---|---|
| class | **Cephalopoda** |
| order | **Dibranchiata** |
| suborder | **Octopoda** |
| family | **Octopodidae** |
| genera & species | **Eledone cirrosa** *lesser octopus* **Octopus vulgaris** *common octopus, others* |

▽ *The ever-changing octopus camouflages itself as coral, altering both its shape and colour.*
▷▽ *The focal point. The well-developed eyes of the octopus have a large cornea which gives them a range of vision of 180 degrees.*

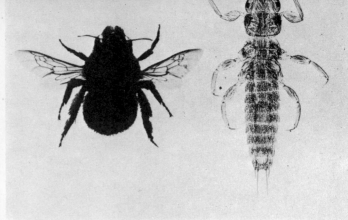

△ A female oil beetle **Meloë proscarabaeus** with a mass of orange eggs she has just laid.

▽ **Meloë proscarabaeus**. Female (below). The functionless wing cases have an unusual overlap.

△ Primary oil beetle larva (right) and the bee which is host to its parasitic childhood.

# Oil beetle

*These small beetles get their name from their habit of exuding an oily fluid from the joints of their legs when disturbed. They belong to the blister beetle family (p 239), and have the same complicated life-cycle, but unlike the brightly-coloured blister beetle, oil beetles are dully-coloured and ugly. They were described by the famous French entomologist Fabre, as 'uncouth beetles . . . their wing cases yawning over their back like the tails of a fat man's coat that is far too tight for their wearer.' This describes the very short wing cases that do not cover the abdomen and which overlap in a way most unusual for a beetle. The wing cases are, in fact, functionless as oil beetles have no wings. A common European oil beetle **Meloë proscarabaeus** is 1 in. long and bluish-black.*

*In the deserts of the southwest United States and Mexico there are some unusual oil beetles, about 1−1½ in. long with very hard bodies and wing cases. The wing cases are fused together and are larger than usual. They reach over the abdomen to form an air chamber. The air in this chamber acts as an insulating barrier against the sun's heat, while the hemispherical shape presents a relatively small surface area for the absorption of heat, and the hard, thick body armour prevents evaporation of the body fluids into the dry desert air.*

### Hitch-hiking thieves

Only a very few oil beetle larvae survive to adulthood as the larval life is extremely complicated. To survive, the larva must manage to hitch a lift, usually on the body of a solitary bee, and then to drop into a cell of its honeycomb. The stout antennae of the adult males of some species, resemble the forceps of an earwig, and are used to clasp the female during mating. As the thousands of eggs develop within her abdomen, the female becomes extremely swollen. Eventually she lays several batches of 3−4 thousand eggs in cracks or holes in the ground. They hatch in 3−6 weeks and thousands of tiny larvae emerge to swarm up the stems of surrounding plants.

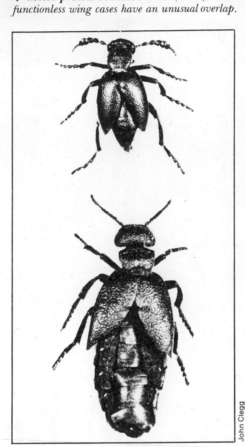

The hatchlings are like lice, with long, narrow bodies, and when they were first discovered hanging to the bodies of bees they were called bee lice. They are very active and scramble up plants to sit in the flowers until a solitary bee visits them. When a bee alights the larvae grip it with their jaws and are carried away. Unfortunately for the larvae they show no discrimination and grasp any hairy insect. Consequently they are often borne away on beetles, flies, butterflies and honeybees. Any that do are doomed, but if they catch hold of the right species of solitary bee, they are eventually carried to the bee's nest. Here they drop off and enter a cell where they devour the bee's egg.

The rest of the larval life is spent in this cell, feeding on the nectar and pollen intended for the growing bee. The louse-like larva undergoes a radical transformation and becomes a soft, helpless creature with short legs, rather like a cockchafer grub. All it does is feed. The spiracles, or breathing holes, are placed high on the back to be clear of the sticky fluid on which the larva is floating. While in the bee's nest the larva sheds its skin several times. At the third moult it is known as the 'pseudo-pupa' and has only minute legs. Two moults later it becomes the true pupa which resembles the adult in form.

The adult oil beetles emerge from the bee's nest in the spring after they entered it as larvae and the complicated cycle starts again. When adult, these beetles feed on plants and are sometimes pests of crops such as potatoes and tomatoes. This very complicated cycle of events with two very different kinds of larvae—one active and one passive—is known as hypermetamorphosis. In other words the oil beetle undergoes more changes in form than the usual larva-pupa-adult stages of other beetles.

In the United States some oil beetles have a simpler, less 'hit-or-miss' life history. The louse-like larvae just run about until they find a mass of locust eggs which they settle in and devour.

## Original dragon's blood

An oil beetle crawling sluggishly through the grass would seem to be utterly defenceless but when handled it exudes an oily, caustic fluid containing cantharidin (see blister beetle, p 239). This fluid is the oil beetle's blood; the beetle's reaction to disturbance is to compress its abdomen and raise its blood pressure so much that the thin skin of the joints is ruptured and blood squirts out. Once the pressure is released, the blood clots quickly. This behaviour is known as 'reflex bleeding' and is practised by several insects, including the ladybird *Coccinella* and certain grasshoppers. Some grasshopper larvae can squirt fluid as much as 2 in. and one produces a foam as air is mixed with the blood. One beetle *Timarcha tenebricosa* is called the bloody-nosed beetle because it ejects red fluid from its mouth when alarmed.

| phylum | **Arthropoda** |
|---|---|
| class | **Insecta** |
| order | **Coleoptera** |
| family | **Meloidae** |
| genera & species | *Meloë proscarabaeus Apulus muralis*, others |

# Oil beetle portraits

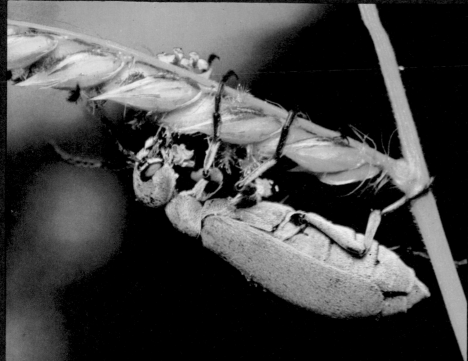

Anthony Bannister: NHPA

◁ *A ½in. long **Epicauta velata** feeding on grass pollen. Oil beetles are often pests, feeding on the foliage of crops, but the beetles of this genus perform a useful function in attacking locust egg pods.*
▽ *An undesirable specimen. Although the oily fluid which a beetle of the **Meloidae** family ejects through its joints does not cause burning blisters, it has an unpleasant taste causing predators to leave it well alone.*

Heinz Schrempp

# Oilbird

*The oilbirds, or guacharos, are remarkable in many ways. They are classified in a suborder of their own, but are related to the nightjars. In appearance they resemble a cross between a nightjar and a hawk. They have an overall length of just over 1 ft but their long, narrow wings span 3 ft. The face, with its discs around the eyes, is very owl-like. The bill is curved like a hawk's and is surrounded by stout bristles at the base. The feet are very weak and oilbirds rarely perch but cling to the sides of rocks like swifts. The plumage is brown, barred with black and spotted with white.*

*Oil birds live in northern South America from Guyana to Peru and also on the island of Trinidad.*

### Ghostly cries

There is a belief among the negroes of Trinidad that oilbirds contain the souls of criminals and other miscreants. This belief arises from the eerie, almost human, cries of the oilbirds as they emerge from caves in the evenings. They roost and nest in the caves in mountain country or on the coast. The roosts are sometimes as much as ½ mile back from the cave entrance, where it is pitch dark. The oilbirds roost on rock ledges during the day and emerge, with grating and piercing shrieks and screams in the evening to feed.

The size of their eyes shows that they have good vision and undoubtedly they rely on sight while out foraging as do nightjars and owls. There is not a glimmer of light in the caves, yet they fly to and from their nests and roosts unerringly. It is now known that they navigate by echo-location in much the same way as bats, except that the sounds they emit are within the range of human hearing. While the oilbirds are flying in the caves a continuous metallic clicking like a typewriter can be heard through the chorus of wails and screams.

### Spicy food

Oilbirds are unique in being the only nocturnal birds that feed on fruit. They may

△ *Banding oilbirds in the caves of Trinidad.*

travel up to 50 miles in search of fruit that they pluck while hovering amongst the foliage and carry back to digest during the day. After the flesh of the fruit is digested, the seeds are regurgitated. By collecting the seeds that had accumulated under the nesting ledges, David Snow was able to determine the kinds of fruit that the Trinidad oilbirds eat. The seeds were mainly those of three kinds of plants: palms, West Indian 'laurels' and incense. The latter two kinds are aromatic and strong-smelling and, as it is known that the part of the brain concerned with smell is well-developed in oilbirds, it may be that they find at least some of their food by smell.

### Slow breeders

The nests are mainly a paste of regurgitated fruit, together with seeds and droppings. They are built on a ledge on a cave wall and as they are used for several years they become quite bulky. The 2–4 eggs in a clutch are laid at quite long intervals and are incubated for 33 days. Most eggs are laid in the early part of the year but new clutches are begun all the year round. The chicks hatch out with a thin covering of down and a thicker coat is grown 3 weeks later. They build up a great store of fat and may be 1½ times as large as an adult. They lose weight when their feathers form.

Oilbird chicks stay on the nest for 14 weeks—an extremely long time. This is probably because they are fed on nothing but fruit flesh which contains very little

protein. Most fruit-eating birds catch insects to provide their young with protein but the young oilbirds have to be content with a long childhood and growing fat from the oily fruit they eat.

### Oil for cooking

In general birds raise their chicks as fast as possible because they are very vulnerable when in the nest. In the depths of the caves the young oilbirds have no natural enemies so the long time spent on the nest is no disadvantage. Man has, however, found a use for the chicks. Their fat can be made into a fine oil that is excellent for cooking purposes and keeps fresh for a year. The South American Indians regularly harvest the young oilbirds, knocking them out of their nests with poles.

## Clicks in the dark

The ability of oilbirds to find their way about in pitch darkness has been studied by Donald Griffin, who is well known for his thorough and exciting studies of echo-location by bats. Griffin visited an oilbird cave in Venezuela and, by exposing photographic film, showed that the oilbirds were able to fly where there was absolutely no light. He showed, with an oscilloscope, that the oilbirds emitted steady trains of clicks at frequencies between 6 000 and 10 000 cycles/second. This is well within the range of human hearing and Griffin was even able to hear the echoes rebounding from the cave walls. To show that the oilbirds really were navigating by echo-location, Griffin released some in a darkened room with cotton wool in their ears. They were completely helpless, but when the cotton wool was removed they avoided flying into walls. Their echo-location is not so sensitive that it can detect flying insects like bats do, but it is certainly sufficient to allow oilbirds to fly through their caves and presumably to locate their nests.

| class | **Aves** |
|---|---|
| order | **Caprimulgiformes** |
| family | **Steatornithidae** |
| genus & species | ***Steatornis caripensis*** |

▽ *Guide lights? The large glowing eyes of the oilbirds give them excellent vision when out foraging for food in the night, but in the dark caves they are only guide lights for inquisitive humans as the oilbirds find their way by echo-location, emitting a rapid series of clicks.*

# Okapi

*The okapi, one of the last big mammals to be discovered in Africa, is the giraffe's only living relative. Its neck is not as long as the giraffe's but the general shape of its body is much the same.*

*It was, however, some time before this was realized and at first scientists thought it might be an ancestor of the horse still surviving. The okapi is a deep velvety, reddish or blackish brown, becoming lighter with age. The face is whitish except for a dark grey crown and forehead, and blackish muzzle. The lower legs are white with black bands around the fetlocks and fore-knees, and a black line down the front of the forelegs. On the upper part of the forelimbs are three or four thick, irregular white stripes and on the upper part of the hindlimbs, and up onto the haunches, are 11–19 equally irregular white stripes. The skin is thick like a giraffe's, about ¼ in., and rubbery. There are glands between the toes. The male has a pair of short horns on the forehead, which are covered with skin and tipped with hair in the young. They develop at about 2 years old. The female has only little knobs here.*

*An adult okapi stands up to 6 ft 1 in. high at the top of the head, 5 ft 5 in. at the shoulder, 5 ft at the rump. Females are usually slightly bigger than males. The weight averages about 550 lb.*

## Rubber-necks

Okapis live in clearings near the river in the Congo rain forests, in an area 140 miles from north to south and 625 miles from east to west; approximately from the Semliki river in the east to Congo-Ubangui junction in the west. Little is known of its behaviour in the wild, except that it moves over well-defined paths. It is thought to be solitary, each possibly holding a territory. Normally placid and friendly, okapis can suddenly become aroused, butting and kicking at their aggressor. This often happens when they are caught.

They eat mainly young shoots and buds, some grass, leaves, fruit and ferns. The food is plucked with the tongue which is long and mobile, like a giraffe's. At the same time the long neck is very supple and the animal can turn its head to lick every part of its body with its tongue.

## Strange habits

The breeding habits are unusual. A pair stays together about 2–3 weeks, the female being in season for 40–50 days. According to Agatha Gijzen, the Antwerp Zoo's biologist, however, the okapi continues to come into heat while she is pregnant, so it was difficult to be sure of the length of gestation, and for some time all that could be said was that it was '9–15 months'. Later observations at Bristol Zoo have, however, shown it to be 435–449 days (about 14½–15 months). This is especially interesting because it is about the same as the giraffe, which is 420–468 days—much longer than any other ruminant.

In many ruminants the mother licks the anus of her calf to make it defaecate, but not the okapi. Of three successive calves born in Bristol Zoo, one did not defaecate until it was 18 days old, a second had not done so by the time it died at 24 days, and the third—which survived—did not do so until its 30th day! Presumably okapi milk is highly nutritious, and contains very little indigestible residue.

## Hard to breed

Up till the 1940's, about twenty okapis had been taken to zoos. Of these only two—one in Antwerp, 1927-1942, and one in London, 1937-1950—lived more than a year or two. In 1948, the Antwerp Zoological Society started to organise the capture of okapis for zoos including a special centre at Epulu, from which breeding pairs were to be sent all over the world.

The first okapi to be born in a zoo was in Antwerp in September 1954, but it only lived a day. Several others born in various zoos did not live long. Then in 1958, one was born in Epulu, and this is still alive, like the one born in the same year in the Paris Zoo. Several okapi calves have died of infections. Bristol Zoo, having lost two calves, decided to move their pregnant female out to a country stable far from infected straw. Its calf survived. At the beginning of 1969 there were 51 okapis in zoos, of which 29 had been born and bred in captivity.

# A pygmy name

Rumours of the okapi's existence reached Europe before 1900. Stanley, long after he met up with Livingstone, wrote in his book 'In Darkest Africa' (1890), 'The Wambutti know a donkey and call it "atti". They say that they sometimes catch them in pits. What they find to eat is a wonder. They eat leaves'. About this time other Europeans had obtained information about the existence of a striped animal in the Ituri forest in the Congo and been given pieces of its skin by pygmies. All of them, however, tended to put it down to a striped antelope of some sort.

Sir Harry Johnston, before going out to Uganda as governor, spoke to Stanley in London about the 'atti' of the Wambutti (Bambuti pygmies). While there he had to journey into the Congo to repatriate a group of pygmies who had entered British territory. On his journey he met Archdeacon Lloyd, of the Boga Mission, the only European to have seen an okapi, and he confirmed what Stanley had told Johnston.

As he travelled, Johnston picked up more tales of the creature. He was able to correct its Bambuti name to 'o'api' (the ' being pronounced like the guttural Arabic 'k'),

▽ *The last big find in Africa—the okapi. A placid and normally friendly animal that leads a solitary life in clearings in the Congo rain forests eating young shoots, buds, grass and fruit.*

▷ *What's it really like up there? Okapi gazes with awe at its nearest living relative—giraffe.*

CAW Guggisberg : WWF

and he concluded that it was a type of zebra in which the upper part of the body was uniform dark brown. Because the pygmies told him that it had more than one hoof, Johnston decided that it must be a survivor of *Hipparion*, the three-toed extinct horse, and when he was shown cloven-hoofed tracks he did not believe they were the okapi's. After trying for a while to get a complete specimen, he purchased two strips of skin which pygmies wore as belts or bandoliers, and sent them to Dr PL Sclater as skin from a new species of zebra living in the Congo forest.

Sclater, secretary of the Zoological Society of London, hastened to communicate this discovery to the Society, and in the Proceedings for Feb. 5th, 1901, he gave the animal the name *Equus (?) johnstoni*. But very shortly afterwards, a Belgian officer named Eriksson, obtained two skulls and a complete skin which showed it to be cloven-hoofed, not odd-toed and horse-like, and also a member of the giraffe family. On June 18th, 1901, Sir Ray Lankester gave it a new name, *Okapia*.

Johnston, finding he had not discovered a surviving *Hipparion*, but determined to be the discoverer of an extinct animal, renamed it *Helladotherium tigrinum*. There is a fossil giraffe named *Helladotherium*, but its skull and teeth are different from those of the living okapi.

Johnston had his rivals, however. The great variability in the stripe pattern of okapis led to several supposed new 'species' being described within a few years of its discovery, and another was claimed in 1939. There is, however, only one true species of okapi, named after its discoverer.

| | |
|---|---|
| class | **Mammalia** |
| order | **Artiodactyla** |
| family | **Giraffidae** |
| genus & species | ***Okapia johnstoni*** |

Wolfgang Lummer

△ *Grooming time at Frankfurt Zoo for two young okapis. The elder one waits patiently for the keeper to give the finishing touches. In 1969 there were 51 okapis in zoos, 29 of which were born and bred in captivity.*

▽ *Sleek profile. Like its relative the giraffe, the okapi has a long, mobile tongue used for plucking food. It also has a fairly long, supple neck and can turn its head to lick every part of its body with its tongue.*

Bavaria

# Olm

*Since it was first made known to science in 1689 the olm has presented many problems to scientists. Olms (the 'l' is pronounced) belong to the same family of amphibians as the mudpuppy. They live in underground rivers and pools and like many other cave-dwelling animals they are blind and lack pigment in the skin. Olms grow to a length of about 1 ft. The eel-like body has a laterally flattened tail and the head is broad with a blunt snout. The legs are very short, with 3 toes on the front legs and 2 on the hind-legs. The eyes are minute and buried in the skin; they cannot be seen in the adult. The body is a translucent white, becoming pinker when the olm is active and blood is flowing through the skin. The three pairs of feathery gills are red.*

*The olm is the only cave-dwelling amphibian in Europe and is restricted to limestone caverns in southeast Europe. It is found in parts of Yugoslavia such as Dalmatia, Herzegovina, Bosnia and Croatia, and in a small area of Italy. It is most common in caverns that form part of the underground course of the River Pivka in Slovenia.*

## Cave-dwellers

The first record of the olm is in a book by the 17th-century Baron Valvasor who recorded that some Yugoslavian peasants ascribed the periodic flooding of the River Bella to a dragon that lived inside a mountain and opened sluice gates when its hideaway was threatened with floods. In the floodwaters the villagers often found lizard-like animals which they took to be the dragon's babies. These animals were olms, and it is only during floods that they are found outside their underground caverns.

Without skin pigment their bodies have no protection from the sun's rays so they soon die when exposed to light.

Inside the caverns, olms live in still pools or in the foaming cascades of the underground rivers where they spend most of their time concealed under boulders. They can, however, swim with great agility and are very difficult to catch. Like newts, olms absorb oxygen through their skin but they also rise to the surface to gulp air. Olms feed on small aquatic animals such as crustaceans and small fish. They are known to be very sensitive to vibrations so they probably detect their prey by the movements they make in the water.

## Losing colour

It is usually impossible to distinguish the sexes of olms but in the breeding season the females become plump and pink. Courtship and mating are similar to that of newts (p 1564), the female picking up a spermatophore deposited by the male. A little later the female lays 30–40 eggs, $\frac{1}{3}$ in. across, over a period of 3 weeks. She coils her body round them, gently waving her tail for aeration and to prevent silt settling on them. After 4 months the larvae, nearly 1 in. long, hatch out. They lack limbs and gills and spend most of their time lying on their sides. Later they become more active and feed on minute algae and crustaceans.

When olms have been kept in water warmer than that of their native caves, they occasionally give birth to live young, the eggs being retained in the female's body until they hatch.

When they hatch young olms are almost black, but as they develop the pigment is gradually lost. Their eyes are also well-developed but they gradually degenerate and sink into the skin, becoming invisible, although the eye muscles and nerves remain. If they are kept in the light from the beginning the colour is retained.

Olms mature at about 10 years and live for at least 25 years.

## Refusing to change

When olms were first discovered our knowledge of the relationships of animals was very imperfect and great difficulty was experienced in fitting the olm into its right place in the animal kingdom. It was once described as a 'doubtful' amphibian, as it had features of both amphibians and fish, and Linnaeus left it out of his *Systema Naturae*. Sir Everard Home, who studied the first fossil *Ichthyosaurus*, even related these two, considering them both to be a kind of fish-lizard or fish-newt. About the same time it was realised that the olm was very like an axolotl (p 111). It was an amphibian that retained its gills throughout life and reproduced in the larval stage — a process known as neoteny.

When it was found that an axolotl could, under certain circumstances, change into a salamander, experiments were carried out on olms to see if they could be induced to change. They all failed, so it seems likely that the olm is not the neotenous larva of another amphibian, as an axolotl is a neotenous salamander, but that it is a wholly aquatic amphibian that has never lived on land. In this case, the olm is a primitive member of the subclass of amphibians, the Urodela or tailed amphibians. Originally the urodeles kept their gills all their lives, then modern types, who spent part of their lives on land, like the newts and salamanders, arose. The olm is, therefore, an evolutionary relic, or 'missing link'.

| class | **Amphibia** |
|---|---|
| order | **Caudata** |
| family | **Proteidae** |
| genus & species | ***Proteus anguinus*** |

▽ *Agile swimmers. Olms are the only cave-dwelling amphibians in Europe. They are blind and lack any pigment in their skin.*

Bavaria

# Opah

The scientific name of this fish means radiant moon, which seems a little strange for such a brilliantly coloured fish. Even its shape belies such a name. It is almost oval in outline, strongly flattened from side to side, up to 6 ft or more long and weighing up to 600 lb. It has a tiny toothless mouth and golden eyes. The single dorsal fin runs from almost the middle of the back nearly to the tail. It is low for most of its length but rises into a high lobe in front. The anal fin is long and low. Both dorsal and anal fins can be folded down into grooves. The pectoral fins are high up on the flanks and above them the lateral line rises in a high curve. The pelvic fins, like the pectorals, are scythe-shaped. The tail, which carries the tail fin, is a short stalk, sharply set off from the rear end of the body.

The opah's colours are hard to describe because they change from green to blue or purple according to the way one looks at the fish. The fins are a vivid scarlet and there is scarlet around the mouth. Light-coloured or silvery spots or flecks are scattered over the body. Willoughby, the 17th-century English naturalist, summed it up by declaring the opah 'the Master of Ceremonies in the Court of Neptune'.

The single species of opah lives in the warmer parts of the Atlantic and Pacific, rarely entering the Mediterranean, but in summer it moves into temperate waters, going as far north in the Atlantic as Newfoundland, Iceland and Norway. In the Pacific it ranges as far north as Alaska. If moonfish is not appropriate, most of its other names are certainly no better: sunfish, kingfish, Jerusalem haddock, San Pedro fish, mariposa, cravo, soho, glancefish and gudlax, a Viking name meaning 'salmon of the gods'. Opah, a West African word, is at least non-committal!

## Another mystery fish

The opah, like the oarfish and the ocean sunfish, is another mystery fish. It is believed to be a deepwater fish because it has often been taken on longlines off Madeira in depths of 150−600 ft. Yet it must spend a fair amount of time at or near the surface because that is where most have been caught. Although its shape would indicate that it is a slow swimmer, PA Orkin in his studies of this fish 20 years ago, found that it feeds largely on small oceanic cuttlefish and squid. These, which Orkin showed to belong to two genera, *Ommastrephes* and *Onychoteuthis*, are among the fastest and most agile of almost any marine animal. This confirms previous reports from examination of the stomach contents, which also showed that crustaceans, especially isopods (marine woodlice) and small fishes are taken. Orkin found as many as 50 beaks of squid in the stomach of one opah.

The stomachs of the fishes he examined contained the bones or otoliths (earbones) of two fishes that live at considerable depths. What we do not know is whether the opah went down to catch these fishes or whether, as so often happens with deep-sea fishes, the fishes had migrated upwards. One surprise item in the stomachs of the opah was a littoral clam *Donax variabilis*, and there is no indication how it came to be there.

When the opah opens its mouth the bones of the upper jaw are shot forward, much as in the John dory (see p 1199). This considerably enlarges the cavity of the mouth so it sucks in its prey. Another peculiarity, which may have something to do with its speed, is that the pectoral fins have a horizontally placed insertion and when they swim the opah is said to beat these up and down like the wings of a bird—an unusual use of the pectoral fins.

## Scanty knowledge

Little is known about their breeding except that the eggs taken from the roe of a captured female were $\frac{1}{30}$ in. diameter, and those taken from another female, which appeared to have finished laying so the eggs left in the ovary were probably fully ripe, were $\frac{1}{10}$ in. diameter. The smallest opah ever caught was taken off the Pacific coast of North America and measured 23 in. long. The next smallest was captured off Bordeaux, in France, and this measured 25 in. long. Opah are usually 30 in. or more long. There is therefore a complete gap in our knowledge of the life of this fish between the egg and the half-grown fish.

## Salmon of the gods

The reason why we have linked the opah with the oarfish and ocean sunfish as being 'mysterious' is that all three are oceanic. Exactly where they normally live is not known for certain and all three turn up from time to time off coasts more or less all over the world. The Vikings named the opah 'salmon of the gods', which seems to fit in with what other people have said about it; that it is an excellent food fish, with red flesh, and a tender, oily, delicate flavour, similar to tunny. It has even been suggested that if we knew more about the opah's breeding grounds and its movements, it might form the basis of an important fishing industry. As it is, nothing is known of its breeding. It is presumed it lays its eggs in deep water and that these eggs rise to the surface well away from coasts, but this is just speculation.

| class | **Pisces** |
|---|---|
| order | **Lampridiformes** |
| family | **Lampridae** |
| genus & species | ***Lampris guttatus*** |

'The Master of Ceremonies in the Court of Neptune'—the opah, **Lampris luna**, is a blaze of colours that change with every angle.

Peter J Green

1578

# Opossum

*The opossums are the only marsupials which live outside Australasia, except for the little known caenolestids or 'rat' opossums of South America. The best known opossum is the Virginia opossum, common in many parts of the United States and ranging into South America. The Virginia opossum is often called the 'possum', but this name is also, confusingly, given to Australian marsupials of the family Phalangeridae such as the brush-tailed opossum (p 295). Virginia opossums are the size of a small dog, with a head and body length of 12–20 in., but their appearance is rat-like with short legs and a pointed muzzle. The tail is almost as long as the body and is naked for most of its length. The ears are also hairless. The rough fur varies from black to brown or white. The hindfeet are rather like human hands. The first toe is clawless and opposable in exactly the same way as our thumb.*

*The other opossums which live in Central and South America are similar to the Virgina opossum in appearance. Some have a bushy tail and the water opossum or yapok, has webbed hindfeet and a waterproof pouch. Most of them are not known at all well, except the murine or mouse opossum that sometimes damages banana and mango crops and is occasionally found in consignments of bananas.*

## Resilient marsupial

The spread, in historic times, of the Virginia opossum from the southeast United States north to Ontario in Canada is remarkable for an animal whose original home is in tropical and subtropical climates. It is even more remarkable when one remembers that it is a marsupial, a group that in most parts of the world has become extinct in face of competition from the placental mammals. The opossum's spread may be due to a decrease in the number of its predators as these have been killed off by man. It is surprising that opossums have survived in the northern parts of their new range as opossums are sometimes found with parts of their ears or tail lost through frostbite. Although they do not hibernate, they become inactive during very cold spells, subsisting on fat stored during the autumn.

Opossums generally live in wooded country where they forage on the ground, climbing trees only to escape enemies such as dogs and sometimes to find food. They can, however, climb well gripping with their opposable toes, while their tail is nearly prehensile. A young opossum can hang from a branch with its tail but adults can use them only as brakes or as a fifth hand for extra support.

Each opossum has a home range of usually 6–7 acres, although it is sometimes twice as large. They feed mainly at night and spend the day in a nest in hollow tree trunks, abandoned burrows, or under piles of dead brushwood. The nest is made of dead leaves that are carried in a most unusual way: they are picked up in the mouth and passed between the front legs to be held between the belly and the tail which is folded under the body.

## Varied diet

Opossums have sometimes been described as scavengers, mainly because they are often found feeding on rubbish around human habitations. This merely shows their adaptability for they will eat a very wide variety of foods. Small ground animals such as earthworms, grasshoppers, beetles, ants, snails and toads are taken in large numbers in the summer and autumn, together with voles, mice, snakes and small birds. Poultry runs are sometimes raided. Plants are eaten especially during late autumn and winter when animal food is becoming scarce and an easy way of finding opossums is to search for them when they are feeding among pokeberries and persimmon at night.

## Carrying the babies

After a gestation of 12–13 days, the tiny young, numbering 8–18, emerge from the mother's body in quick succession and crawl into her pouch to grasp her nipples. As she usually has 13 nipples, some of the litter may be doomed to perish from the start. The young remain in the pouch for 10 weeks, and after this they sleep huddled together in the nest. When the mother goes out foraging she carries the youngsters, now the size of rats, clinging to her back, and if she has a large litter, she may find it difficult to walk. The young are weaned shortly afterwards and they become independent when about 14 weeks old. Females breed before they are 1 year old, producing one litter in the northern part of their range but two or three in the south. The usual life span in the wild is about two years.

## Good to eat?

Opossums are eaten by many animals such as bobcats, coyotes, foxes, hawks and owls. They are trapped for their fur which is not of very good quality but is used to make simulated beaver or nutria. In some places they are eaten and 'possum and sweet taters' is highly esteemed by some. One writer states, however, that it is best to throw away the possum and eat the 'taters'.

# Playing possum

The phrase 'playing possum' has come from the amazing habit of opossums of feigning death when frightened. The habit is not confined to opossums and has been recorded in foxes, African ground squirrels and the hog-nosed and grass snakes. When an opossum is confronted by a predator such as a dog, and cannot escape quickly, it turns at bay, hissing and growling, and trying to attack. If the dog succeeds in grabbing and shaking the opossum, it suddenly goes limp, rolling over with eyes shut and tongue lolling out as if dead. Strangely enough, the dog then loses interest and presumably this is the case with natural preda-

*Wide-eyed beauty — the murine opossum, a pretty creature about the size of a large mouse, is a tree-living animal. It is quick-witted and completely fearless, opening its mouth at anything that threatens, and sometimes forgetting to close it for half an hour or more!*

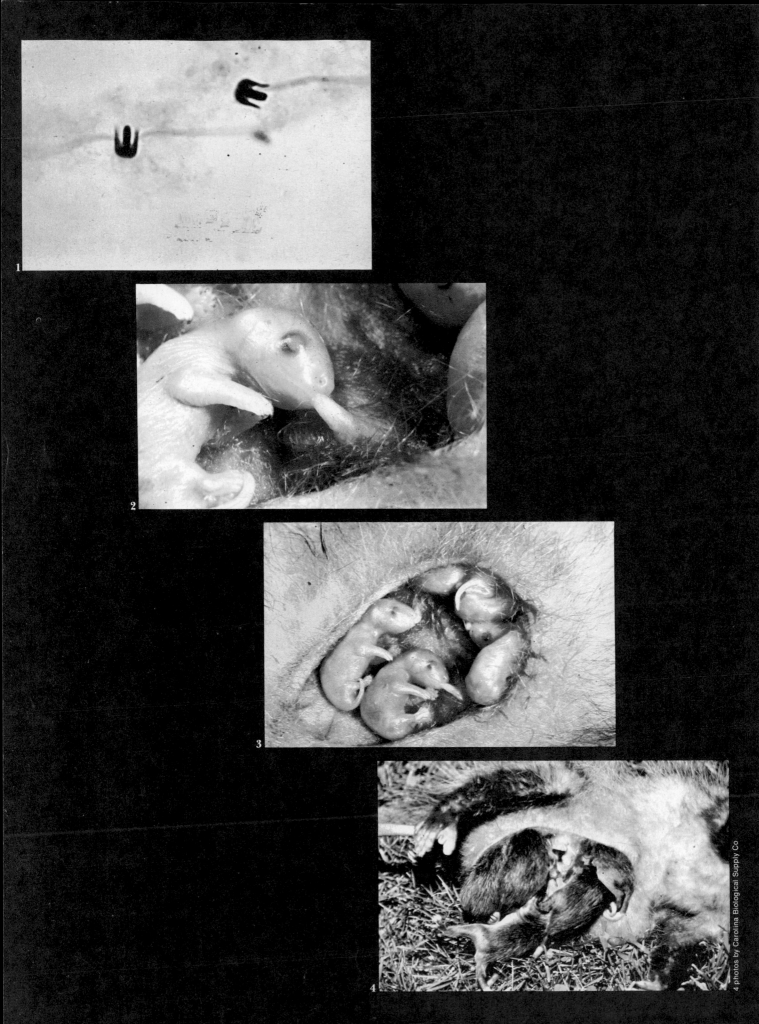

tors that do not eat carrion, that is dead animals. A few minutes later the opossum gradually recovers and runs off.

We can only presume that this strange trick is effective in persuading predators to leave opossums, otherwise the opossums would only be playing into the predators hands. It is also a complete mystery as to how the trick is worked. It has been suggested that paralysing substances are released into the brain to produce the death-like state and these gradually diffuse away so the opossums recover. More recently experiments have been made with an electro-encephalogram, a machine which records the patterns of minute electric currents in the brain, showing differences between waking and sleeping states for instance. Recordings made of opossums feigning death showed that they are, in fact, in a 'normal, waking, highly alert behavioural state'. They are not in a trance or catalepsy, but wide awake, so they are really living up to their name and 'playing possum'.

| class | **Mammalia** |
|---|---|
| order | **Marsupialia** |
| family | **Didelphidae** |
| genera & species | **Chironectes minimus** water opossum **Didelphis marsupialis** Virginia opossum **Marmosa murina** murine opossum others |

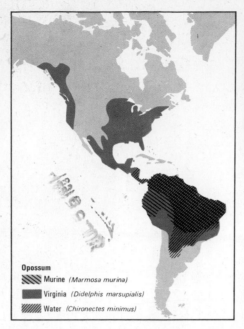

**Opossum**

▨ Murine (*Marmosa murina*)
▨ Virginia (*Didelphis marsupialis*)
▨ Water (*Chironectes minimus*)

◁ *Opossums are strictly American — the only marsupials bar caenolestids outside Australasia.*
*1 The opossum has oddly-shaped spermatozoa as this photomicrograph shows. (1 000 × life size.)*
*2 Naked embryo-like young opossum attached by its mouth-slit to its mother's teat.*
*3 Litter in the pouch. The young have partly-developed limbs and rudimentary eyes and ears.*
*4 Young still in the pouch but now covered with fur and with well-developed limbs.*

*Life-line — the Virginia opossum looks stranded but don't be deceived for it can hang from a branch by its naked, scaly, prehensile tail for considerable periods (above).*
*Good-natured mother allows her young to scramble over her (below). This opossum,*
*Marmosa sp, does not have a pouch. It can breed three times a year in the cooler parts of its range, and all the year round in tropical areas.*

Atlas Photo

1581

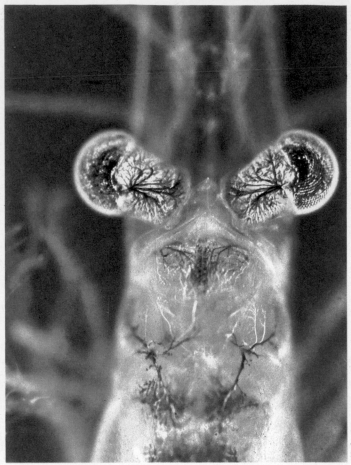

△ *Delicate transparency, a dorsal view of* **Neomysis** *exposes all the body regions including the fine and varied appendages of the thorax.*

△ *Head of* **Neomysis***, its large bulbous eyes are composed of two layers behind which can be seen the branching pigmented chromatophore cells.*

# Opossum shrimp

*These are small shrimp-like crustaceans, the females of which have a brood pouch or marsupium to hold their eggs and young, rather like the opossum. The name is often applied to all the species in the order Mysidacea — nearly 400 of them — or it may be reserved for those of the genus* **Mysis***. Most of the Mysidacea are marine, with about 25 species living in fresh water and twice that number in brackish water.*

*The typically shrimp-like body is divided into a thorax and an abdomen. The thorax consists of 8 segments covered, except at the rear, by a carapace fused with the head and the first 3 segments. The abdomen, made up of 6 segments, ends in a tail fan, which bears, in most species, a pair of balancing organs characteristic of the group. These are little chambers in each of which, on a group of sensory hairs, sits a mass consisting partly of calcium fluoride. There are two pairs of antennae on the head. The stalked and movable compound eyes are absent in a few cave-dwelling species. Most opossum shrimps are $\frac{1}{5}-1$ in. long, though some are as short as $\frac{1}{8}$ in. or as long as $7\frac{1}{2}$ in. As a general rule, the length increases from shallow to deep water and from the tropics to the poles.*

*The colour varies from species to species. It may be deep red in the deep seas, bright green in shallow waters, perhaps to match a bright green seaweed, very dark or nearly transparent, and so on. The colour is also inclined to vary with the background, with which the opossum shrimps tend to harmonize. Colour changes are caused by the movement of pigments inside groups of cells called chromatophores.*

*Opossum shrimps are very important as food for other fishes and they are sold for human consumption in the Far East. They are not, however, used much in the West. In Jersey they have for a long time been made into a paste called chervé for use as bait for mullet.*

## Sink or swim

Opossum shrimps are denser than water and must keep swimming if they are not to sink. While some are entirely pelagic, most species swim near the bottom by day, often tending to rise towards the surface at night. In addition to the normal swimming patterns, opossum shrimps can, when disturbed, spring suddenly backwards by flexing the abdomen and tail fan under the thorax and suddenly straightening it again. They can do this so powerfully that they can jump right out of the water. One species *Gastrosaccus spinifer* half walks and half swims over the bottom and rapidly buries itself in sand if disturbed.

## Filter feeders

Most opossum shrimps feed by filtering fine particles of dead plants and animals as well as microscopic organisms from the water, but larger foods — living or dead — may also be eaten by some species. The filter feeders draw water currents in towards the mouth by the vibration of appendages on the head called maxillae each of which ends in a filtering comb of bristles. In many species the maxillae are helped by the beating of the thoracic limbs. Currents of water are also set up when the shrimp is swimming and when it is breathing, but there is no single pattern for all opossum shrimps. For example, some species swim with their thoracic limbs and some with the swimmerets on the abdomen. Where gills are present, they may be on the thorax or the abdomen. Some opossum shrimps have no gills but breathe through their carapace, which· is rich in blood vessels.

## Stay-at-home young

The breeding habits are known for only a few of the opossum shrimps. The most characteristic feature is the protection of the young in the shelter of a brood pouch on the underside of the thorax of the female. In mating, the male approaches the underside of the female, himself upside down, facing in the same or opposite direction. The male places sperm into the brood pouch either through a long genital tube or, in some species, he merely sheds his sperm and lets water currents carry them into the

△ *A good mother, the female opossum shrimp carries her young in a brood pouch under her body.*
▽ *Looking like a boiled shrimp* **Gnathophausia** *exhibits the red colour typical of deep-sea mysids.*

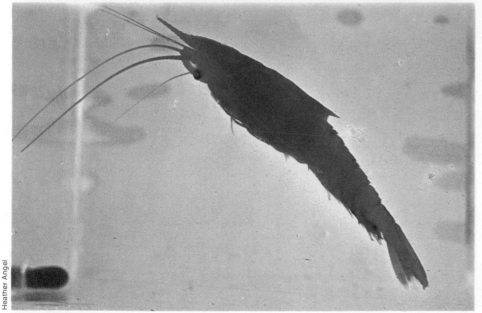

**Opossum shrimp** *(Mysis relicta)*

brood pouch. The female then lays her eggs in the brood pouch 20—30 minutes later where they are fertilised. Usually two to several dozen eggs are laid. The young stay in the pouch for a few days to a few months after hatching, the time depending on the species and the temperature. They are liberated during the evening or early night and the female then moults and mates again the same night. Opossum shrimps usually live for one or two years.

## Ice Age relict

The few opossum shrimps that have invaded fresh water are restricted to localities near the coast where they are subject to sea spray. The most widely distributed freshwater species is also the only one that is found in the British Isles, though here it is found only in Lake Ennerdale and a few lakes in Ireland, including Lough Neagh, where it is important as food for pollan fish, and in Lough Erne, Lough Corrib and Lough Derg. This species *Mysis relicta*, $\frac{3}{8}$ in.—1 in. long, has a curious distribution, for elsewhere it is found only in the brackish waters of the Baltic and in certain freshwater lakes in Denmark, northern Germany, Sweden, Norway, Finland and North America, including some of the Great Lakes. In North America it is very important as food for whitefish and chub. It has occasionally been found in the sea outside the Baltic, but such specimens were probably washed there from fresher water. The name *M. relicta* can be translated as 'the opossum shrimp that was left behind', a relict from the changes that took place during the Ice Ages. A few other crustaceans have a similar distribution and there has naturally been speculation as to how they have come to be where they are. The idea generally held is that the species arose in a salt water lake formed when some of the Arctic Ocean was impounded by glaciation in what is now the Soviet Union, between the rivers Ob and Yenisei. As the water became fresher the population of shrimps became adapted to the change and gave rise to *Mysis relicta*. (It is of interest to note that there is a marine species *M. oculata* so like *M. relicta* that the two were once regarded as varieties of a single species.) Subsequently the freshwater species *M. relicta* spread from lake to lake along the retreating ice margin east to America and west to the Baltic. Its presence in Ennerdale is, however, still unexplained. Probably it got there during the last Ice Age, but it could have got there much earlier. Because of its origin, *M. relicta*, like other animals with the same kind of distribution, is known as a 'glacial relict'.

| | |
|---|---|
| phylum | **Arthropoda** |
| class | **Crustacea** |
| sub-class | **Malacostraca** |
| super-order | **Peracarida** |
| order | **Mysidacea** |
| family | **Mysidae** (and other families) |
| genus & species | *Mysis oculata* *M. relicta* |

# Orang utan

*The orang utan is one of our more interesting relatives. It occupies an intermediate place within the Hominoidea, the superfamily that comprises the apes and man, as it is less closely related to man than the gorilla or chimpanzee, but more man-like than the gibbon.*

*The big male orang stands 4½ ft high when upright, and may weigh as much as a man. Females stand only 3 ft 10 in. at the most, and weigh half as much as the male. The arms are 1½ times as long as the legs, both hands and feet are long and narrow and suited for grasping, and the thumb and great toe are very short since they would only 'get in the way' of the hook-like function of the hand. The skin is coarse and dark grey, and the hair, which is reddish, is sparse, so the skin can be seen through it in many places. The male develops large cheek-flanges of unknown function, and grows a beard or moustache, the rest of the face being virtually hairless. There is a great deal of variation in facial appearance; orangs are as individual and instantly recognisable as human beings. Both sexes have a laryngeal pouch, which in the male can be quite large, giving it a flabby appearance on the neck and chest. The forehead is high and rounded, and the jaws are prominent. Youngsters have a blue tinge to the face.*

*Orang utans are found on Borneo and Sumatra. There are slight differences between the two races, and these are more marked in the male. The Borneo race is maroon-tinted, and the male looks really grotesque, with enormous cheek-flanges and great dewlaps formed by the laryngeal sac. The Sumatran race is slimmer and lighter-coloured, and males can look quite startlingly human, with only small flanges and sac, a long narrow face, and a long gingery moustache.*

## Old man of the woods

The orang utan is strictly a tropical forest animal. It generally lives in low-lying, even swampy forests, but is also found at 6 000 ft on mountains in Borneo. Here, at any rate, most individuals are entirely arboreal. They swing from branch to branch by their arms, though they may use their feet as well, or walk upright along a branch, steadying themselves with their hands round the branch above. It is reported by the Dyaks of Borneo that big old males become too heavy to live in the trees, so they spend most of their time on the ground.

When they are on the ground, orangs move quadrupedally, with the feet bent inwards and clenched, and the hands either clenched or flat on the ground. This contrasts with the gorilla and chimpanzee, which live mainly on the ground and 'knuckle-walk', with their feet flat on the ground and their hands supported on their knuckles. In captivity, orangs easily learn—or discover for themselves—how to walk erect, but because the leg muscles are insufficiently developed to do this easily, the knee is kept locked and the leg straight.

## Anti-social 'burping'

At night the orang utan makes a nest, between 30 and 70 ft above the ground. There is often a kind of sheltering roof over this nest, to protect the orang from the rain—a structure which is not found in nests made by chimps or gorillas. The nest is otherwise much more sketchily made than that of chimps or gorillas. It takes only 5 minutes to make and the orang usually moves on and makes a new nest at its next night's stopping place. Sometimes the same one is used again and the previous night's nest may be used for a daytime nap.

△ *An aggressive orang utan burps defiantly.*

Toni Angermayer

Unlike gorillas and chimpanzees, orang utans seem to have no large social groupings. A female with her infant often travels with other such females for a while, forming something like a smaller version of the chimpanzee's 'nursery group'. A male may join this group, but adult males live alone most of the time. Adolescents of both sexes tend to travel around in groups of twos or threes. It is possible that male orangs, like gibbon families, may be territorial, spacing themselves vocally. The laryngeal sac is filled with air, making the animal swell up terrifyingly, and the air is then released to produce what has been described as a 'loud, two-tone booming burp'. They communicate within a group by making a smacking sound with their lips every few seconds. The most terrifying sound which an orang makes is a roar. This begins on a high note and the tone gets deeper and deeper as the laryngeal sac fills with air. Roaring is heard at night and before dawn, and orangs are said to make the same noise when wounded. The Dyaks report that male orangs fight and scars are quite common.

There is no special birth season, food being available all the year round in the Indonesian rain forest. Gestation lasts 9 months. The young orang weighs only 3½—4 lb at birth, and is sparsely covered with hairs on the back and head. At first it clings to its mother's fur, usually slung on her hip, but when it is a little older, it wanders about on its own, sometimes walking along the branch behind its mother, clinging to her rump hairs. At about 5 years or so, orangs seem to leave their mothers and form adolescent bands.

## Not olive branches!

Man is the principal enemy of the orang utan. Orangs love the juicy, evil-smelling durian fruit, and so do human beings, so this is often a source of contention. An orang will react to a human intruder by making a great deal of the smacking sound, and breaking off branches, keeping up a continuous shower of them which is often annoying enough to drive the humans away. A Dyak recently reported that he was attacked for no reason by a huge male orang that he came upon unexpectedly on the ground. It has few other enemies. There are no tigers in Borneo—Dyaks claim to have exterminated them about 1 000 years ago—and in Sumatra there are only a few. Leopards are unknown on both islands.

## Zoos are a danger

The orang's distribution has been steadily declining. Its ancestors' remains have been found in 14 million-year-old deposits in the Siwalik Hills, Punjab, India. In the Pleistocene, 500 000 years ago, the orang was found as far north as China, and as far south as Java. Today it occurs all over Borneo—the largest and least populated of the East Indian islands—and in the north of Sumatra. It seems that deforestation and heavy human populations have affected its distribution very adversely and there are now fears that it may become extinct altogether in the wild. One reason for its decline is its slow breeding rate. A female breeds every fourth year or so, and usually not until the previous young has left her. It is possible that the average female may bear only three or four young in her life.

The biggest threat, however, to the orang's survival is, sad to say, the zoo trade. Every zoo wants a young ape to display to its visitors, and orangs are the easiest to obtain. Many unscrupulous private zoos, especially in the United States, have paid high prices for baby orangs, and there has been quite a lucrative trade in them in Southeast Asia. Baby orangs are obtained by shooting their mothers. The dealer does not make much effort to ensure the captive's welfare as he probably bought it from the hunter at a low fee, so many youngsters die. For every one orang that reaches a zoo alive, ten orangs—mothers and other babies—have quite probably perished. It is now illegal in Singapore to possess orangs, and smugglers are penalised, but other ports in Southeast Asia are still open for this trade. A law is at present under consideration, or may already have been passed, in the United States, to forbid the import of rare animals, such as orang utans, and this may have some effect on the situation. The deforestation problem, however, remains.

In 1963 Barbara Harrisson estimated that only 2 000 wild orangs remained in Sabah, 1 000 in Kalimantan (Indonesian Borneo),

▷ *A young orang secure in its mother's arms.*

Wolfgang Lummer

Wolfgang Lummer

*Growing old. Youngsters (above) stay with their mother for 5 years but they are 10 or 12 before they are mature (below) and they may live to 40.*

Toni Angermayer

700 in Sarawak and 1 000 in Sumatra. Of these, only the Sabah population seems to be anything like adequately protected. In 1964 another estimate put the Sumatra population at only 100. Tom and Barbara Harrisson undertook a programme in Sarawak of reintroducing into the wild, young orangs which had been illegally bought by people. This has met with a certain amount of success. There are about 300 in zoos all over the world and breeding has been achieved several times, but the rearing of the young is not too easy. Most zoos that breed them have now adopted a policy of keeping the Bornean and Sumatran races separate, which will help to save the Sumatran race.

| class | **Mammalia** |
|---|---|
| order | **Primates** |
| family | **Pongidae** |
| genus & species | ***Pongo pygmaeus pygmaeus*** *Bornean orang utan* |
| | ***P. p. abeli*** *Sumatran orang utan* |

△ *Brotherly love.* ▽ *The old man of the woods. A male orang with his large cheek flanges.*

*Four poses of an orang utan. These forest-dwelling animals swing through the trees on their long arms, which, when hanging loose, reach almost to their feet. Both their hands and feet are long and narrow, and the thumb and great toe short. They usually grip the branches with their fingers although they sometimes walk upright along a branch on their feet, using their hands to steady themselves.*

# Orb spider

*Orb spider is a collective name for those spiders belonging to the family Argiopidae that spin an orb-shaped web, sometimes called a cartwheel or geometric web. These spiders, with their bodies large by comparison with their legs, are entirely dependent on their webs to catch their prey. The most numerous and most studied orb spider in Europe is the European garden spider, also known as the diadem or cross spider.*

*The female is ½ in. long, excluding the legs, the male is about half this, although the sizes reached by males are variable. The colour of the body may vary from a drab pale fawn to a rich brown. It may have little patterning on the abdomen or it may be marked with spots, blotches and lines in white, yellow or shades of brown. The most characteristic of the markings is, in its simplest form, a group of five whitish spots forming a cross. This pattern may be extended into a series of spots or oval markings. Even in pale spiders, the cross shows up in a photograph.*

## How the web is built

All spiders live by eating other animals, usually insects. Most of them construct some form of snare made of silk threads given out from a group of spinnerets on the underside near the tip of the abdomen. In orb spiders the web or snare starts with an outer scaffolding. The first thread laid down is known as the bridge thread. It is horizontal and uppermost. Then two side threads are joined to it and, often, a fourth to complete the rectangle. This last thread may be missing when, as sometimes happens, the spider builds a triangular or polygonal frame. A set of radial threads is then laid down, from the frame to a hub in the centre. At the hub a closely woven platform is made from which a spiral of temporary scaffolding is run outwards. All this is made of non-sticky silk and the snare itself is laid down on it. Using the non-sticky threads to walk on, the spider, working from without inwards, lays down the close spiral of sticky threads, distinguished by the beads along each thread. As the spider is making the sticky snare it cuts away the temporary scaffolding as it goes.

It is a popular idea that the silk is liquid when first given out of the spinnerets and that it hardens on contact with the air. In

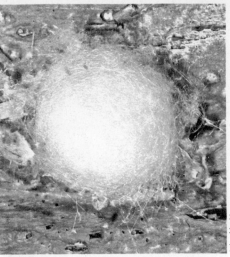

John Markham

△ *Looking like a discarded candyfloss this delicate yellow ball is in fact a silken cocoon containing about 600 garden spider eggs. The spider fastens its cocoon under a large leaf, window-sill or anywhere that is secluded.*
▽ *Jewelled abdomen—the unmistakable markings on the abdomen of the garden spider show clearly why it is often called diadem spider and cross spider.*

Aldo Margiocco

fact it coagulates as it is being squirted out and becomes strong and extensile as the spider pulls on it.

## Webs as fishing nets

When the web is complete the spider retires to a hiding place, perhaps under a leaf, somewhere on the outer scaffolding. When an insect flies into the web and struggles the spider is alerted by the vibrations and runs out to secure its victim, usually swath-

have used these webs for fishing nets, bending a pliable stick into a loop with a handle and passing this through a web so it comes away attached to the loop.

## When spiderlings leave home

Eggs are laid in autumn in silken cocoons of a dingy golden-yellow colour, more or less oval, 1½ in. long, each cocoon containing 600 – 800 eggs. The cocoons are fastened under large leaves, a window sill, plank

ence between male and female, but after a while the females begin to grow more quickly. They do not mature until the following summer, and then growth in size is very rapid, the females outstripping the males and making webs 2 ft across. This is why the orb webs seem suddenly to appear in late summer. The spiders have been there all the time, but they and their webs have suddenly grown large. The majority do not survive the first frosts and by the end of

△ *Bejewelled diadem. A garden spider in the centre of its dewdrop-laden web, having every reason to be proud of its geometric magnificence.*
◁ *Deceptive beauty. Surrounded by morning mist, spiders' webs shimmer with dewdrops which will soon evaporate to leave the traps invisible.*

Okapia

ing it in silk. At the same time it injects poison into it from its fangs (chelicerae) which not only paralyses the prey but acts as a digestive juice liquefying the contents of the body. Later, the spider inserts its fangs into the victim's body and uses them as tubes for sucking out the liquid. Although insects are the main prey of spiders the larger species may catch small birds, even bats, in their webs. Tropical species of *Nephila*, for example, spin webs between trees and these may be as much as 8 ft across and made of thick, tough silk. In parts of southeast Asia the local peoples

or inverted flower pot, anywhere that offers a secluded corner. The eggs hatch the following June and the spiderlings, as soon as they are hatched, spin an irregular mass of almost invisible strands of silk in which they cluster in a ball. When disturbed they rush about in all directions coming together again in a ball once things have settled down. They stay together in this way for a few days then start to scatter.

As each arrives on a new site it spins a small orb web about 2 in. across similar to the familiar 'cartwheel' but much more irregular. At this time there is little differ-

November even the hardiest of adults have died. A few pass the winter in sheltered spots and occasionally a diadem spider will stay in a house.

## Climate the worst enemy

In temperate latitudes at least the weather is the spider's worst enemy, especially drought and excessive rain. The orb spinners are less preyed upon than those spiders living nearer the ground but there are many small birds that include spiders in their normal diet. Insects such as the parasitic wasps and ants also prey on them. There is

△ **Argyope**, a South African orb spider swathes a butterfly in silk to disable it.

△ *Signature spider is the local name for* **Argyope** *as it makes a silk zig-zag in its web.*

△ *Silken canopy, but the beauty is deceiving for this is a snare for unsuspecting victims.*

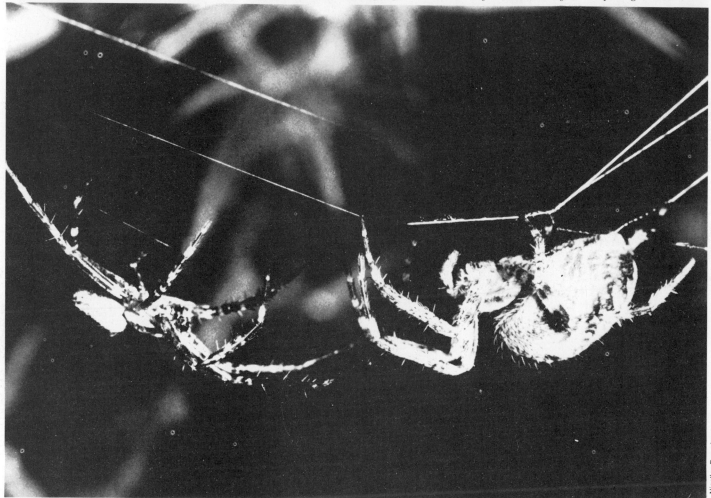

△ *Experienced tight-rope walkers: the male garden spider (left)  makes his first tentative advances towards the lady of his choice  (right)*

a certain amount of cannibalism as well, the best known of which is when the female eats her mate.

## Does she eat her mate?

Many people tend to think that once the male has mated he is eaten by the female. This idea has been held for so long that it is now accepted as the rule. But one expert after another has declared that this is a great exaggeration.

The leading British expert on spiders,

WS Bristowe, in *The World of Spiders,* writes: 'Having survived the threats of starvation, climate and enemies the male spider, if he is a web-builder, abandons his web, and spends his time searching for females and courting them, often with little effort devoted in between whiles to feeding himself. His remaining span of life is usually short, and post-mortem investigations would show that death was in most cases due to exhaustion and under-nourishment rather than to slaughter by the females as is commonly supposed. Such tragedies do

occur but are comparatively rare.' The mere fact that a male usually mates with more than one female should be proof enough that the popular notion of 'the female spider eating her husband' is unfounded.

| phylum | **Arthropoda** |
|---|---|
| class | **Arachnida** |
| order | **Araneae** |
| genus & species | ***Araneus diadematus*** <br> *European garden spider* |

# Oribi

*The oribi is one of the small, straight-horned dwarf antelopes, closely related to the gazelles. It is one of the largest of this group, 20—28 in. at the shoulder, with silky hair, glandular knee-tufts, and a bushy black tail. The coat is grey-fawn to tawny, orange or rufous, white below and with white partial rings round the eyes. There is a dark bare patch of skin below each ear, rather like that of the reedbuck, and a gland in the corner of each eye.*

*Oribis are found in Africa from the Sudan to the Cape, as far as 13°N in central and western Ethiopia, Lake Chad and Senegal. Until the spread of European settlement they were abundant, but are now extinct in many areas.*

### Living in small groups

Oribis live in open grassland, on rolling downs, and in bush country. They are diurnal preferring to feed in the early morning, often coming out before sunrise, then lying up in the grass after 6—7 am. Around noon oribis can often be seen standing or lying in tall grass, or lying up in hollows. They usually go around in pairs, but groups of up to six have been seen.

### The Laufschlag gesture

The rutting season is in the early part of the year. Gestation is about 210 days, and the young are born from September to January according to the part of Africa in which the oribi lives. Oribis set up territories, each pair or family party living in an area of ½—1 sq mile. The boundaries are marked to keep other oribis away. When the female defaecates or urinates, the male stamps in the ordure, so presumably imparting scent from glands between his front hoofs. He also spreads the waxy secretion from his eye-glands by wiping it onto twigs or stems. This must convey an individual 'atmosphere' to the territory and if one pair are removed another pair will move in within a day or two. In the courting ceremony the male raises his foreleg and strokes the female's hindleg. This action is called the Laufschlag gesture, very typical of gazelles and their relatives. He follows the female as she walks slowly along with tail held erect. Occasionally the male rises on his hindlegs as if to mount, but the female continues walking. After some 15 minutes the male stretches his head forward, pushes it between the female's hindlegs and lifts her rear end off the ground. He trundles her forward on her front legs for a few paces. He then withdraws his head, examines and sniffs her genitalia, and pushes his head under again. After this has been repeated two or three times, the female stands still. Now the male mounts and mates with her. It seems that the 'pushing under' is the direct stimulus to mating; after the male has performed this act a couple of times, the female permits mating.

As with all small antelopes, the young grow quickly, doubling the birth weight after 3 weeks. The fawns hide in the long grass and the mother moves away from it as a diversionary tactic at any sign of danger. Full size is reached at about 8 months.

### Running and jumping

Oribis are small animals and subject to predation by lions and even small cats, as well as pythons and eagles. They sleep lightly and wake easily to the shrill whistling alarm call and gallop off with a stiff gait, rumps bobbing up and down. As the oribi runs its tail is held stiffly up, wagging. There are frequent 'stotting' episodes, behaviour seen in many gazelles and dwarf antelopes, in which the animal jumps into the air with all four legs straight and stiff. It serves at once to give the animal a better view, to warn others visually and allow them to follow. After dashing off a hundred yards or so, the oribis stop and turn to watch the source of the disturbance, fleeing again if danger still threatens.

## Steadfast oribi

One possible reason for the great decrease in numbers of oribis lies in their faithfulness to their territories. When disturbed they tend to circle back to the place where they started from, so presenting an easy target. They are also very curious and will approach an unfamiliar object, even an armed man, advancing cautiously, stopping and advancing again. When a forest fire sweeps through their territory the pair will flee, but return behind the wall of flames presumably to subsist on pockets of vegetation left by the fire or on quick growing grasses and herbs that shoot up through the ashes.

| class | **Mammalia** |
|---|---|
| order | **Artiodactyla** |
| family | **Bovidae** |
| genus & species | ***Ourebia ourebia*** |

L. Lee Rue III: Photo Res

Jane Burton: Photo Res

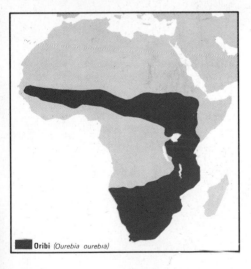

■ Oribi (*Ourebia ourebia*)

◁◁ *A quick glance over his back to see if all is clear. The oribi is a small antelope and much preyed upon. When it is pursued it gallops off for a hundred yards or so and then stops to turn round and watch his pursuer, fleeing again if danger is still imminent.*
◁ *Staking his claim. The male oribi marks his territory by wiping the waxy secretion from his eye-glands onto twigs and stems. Overleaf: In the heat of the day an oribi poses for the camera. Only the males have horns that are short and spikelike and rise straight from the dome of the head. Oribis have very slender legs and skip along on the tips of their small hoofs.*

# Oriole

The name oriole is derived from the Latin word **aureolus** meaning golden and is applied to a family of birds of which the golden oriole is the best known. This is a very striking bird, slightly larger than a song thrush. The male is a golden yellow with black wings and tail, with outer tail feather-tips yellow. The female is less gaudy, with the yellow of the head and back replaced by olive-green. The underparts are lighter and streaked with brown and the wings and tail are mainly brown. The golden oriole breeds in most of Europe south of the Baltic, the northwest tip of Africa and in many parts of Central

fused with the 'American orioles' of the family Icteridae. That family includes the grackles, cowbirds, oropendolas, meadowlarks and several other groups including the orioles of the genus **Icterus**, from the Latin word for yellow.

### Forest birds

Orioles are forest birds, usually seen singly or in pairs. The exceptions are the figbirds which live in flocks. Golden orioles are not easy to observe as they are shy birds living in the treetops. In England, where it is an infrequent visitor, the golden oriole is sometimes confused with the green woodpecker. When the greenish-yellow rump of the latter is seen disappearing through the trees, it often gives rise to excited reports of orioles. Golden orioles migrate south-

the nest for a fortnight; both parents help with the incubation, feeding and rearing the young.

## Secretive songsters

Although their plumage is so striking orioles are usually inconspicuous among the foliage of trees, but their presence is given away by their fluting, bubbling songs, and some species such as the blackheaded oriole of Africa, are accomplished mimics, imitating the songs of other birds. In his book *A Study of Bird Song,* the Rev EA Armstrong has suggested that there is a link between the vocal abilities of the golden oriole and its shy, woodland habits. The jay is another noisy woodland bird and the tawny owl which lives in denser woods than most other owls is also the most vocal. There are,

△ A sunshine bird: the golden oriole is a summer visitor to Europe, sometimes breeding in England.

△ Golden oriole at its hammock-like nest.

Asia and the Indian sub-continent. It visits the southern counties of England mostly in the spring, but has very rarely bred there.

There are about 28 species of orioles. The golden oriole is the only European one. The others are found in Africa, Asia and Australia. They range in size from that of a starling to that of a jay. They are usually brightly coloured with the males brighter than the females. The black oriole of Borneo is an exception, being completely black except for chestnut under the tail. The maroon oriole that ranges from the Himalayas to Formosa has maroon plumage except for black head, neck and wings. In Australia and New Guinea there live the two figbirds, rather different in character from the other orioles. They have a naked patch of skin around the eye and a short bill. The yellow figbird of northern Australia has an olive-green back, yellow underparts and a black head with a ring of red skin around the eye. The blackish tail is edged with white.

The orioles of the family Oriolidae that live in the Old World should not be con-

wards in the winter. Those that nest in Europe move across the Mediterranean and Sahara to tropical and southern Africa and Madagascar. Other species of oriole are also migratory unless they live in evergreen forests.

### Insects and fruit

During the breeding season in particular orioles are insect-eaters, catching beetles, especially cockchafers, caterpillars, bugs, grasshoppers and flies. They are among the few birds that eat woolly caterpillars, first beating them against a branch to wipe off the hairs. Later in the season orioles eat fruit such as cherries, grapes and berries; and around the Mediterranean large quantities of figs are eaten.

### Difficult to study

Study of the breeding habits of orioles has been difficult because of their shy habits. The eggs of some species have not even been described. The nest of the golden oriole is a remarkable hammock-like structure slung between two horizontal branches. It is built, mainly by the female, from grasses, sedges and strips of bark. The eggs are white with a few purplish spots. The three or four eggs hatch in 2 weeks. The chicks stay in

perhaps, two reasons for this link. In dense cover birds have to advertise themselves to potential mates or rivals by sound rather than by visual displays and a bird can afford to be noisy in dense cover because it is well hidden from predators or can slip away from them easily. Of course, this correlation does not always hold true as there are other factors to be considered. For instance, birds can be noisy in the open if they are too large or too fast for predators. When considering the familiar songbirds such as the blackbird which often sings in full view it is as well to remember that its original home was in the dense forests that once covered Britain and Europe and not in the isolated trees of modern suburbia.

| class | **Aves** |
| --- | --- |
| order | **Passeriformes** |
| family | **Oriolidae** |
| genus & species | ***Oriolus hosii*** *black oriole* ***O. oriolus*** *golden oriole* ***O. trailli*** *maroon oriole* ***O. xanthornus*** *blackheaded oriole* ***Sphecotheres flaviventris*** *yellow figbird* *others* |

# Oropendola

The oropendolas are known in America as orioles but they belong to the icterids, which include such diverse birds as the cowbirds, caciques (pronounced ka-seeks), grackles, bobolinks, military starlings and meadowlarks. The family ranges throughout the Americas, the bobolink nesting in Canada and the military starling in the Falkland Islands, but most icterids, including the oropendolas, are tropical.

The best-known oropendola is the Montezuma oropendola of Mexico to Panama. It is the largest oropendola, about the size of a crow. The males are 19 in. long, the females considerably smaller. The plumage is very striking with black head, neck and chest, chestnut body and wings and tail brownish-black with bright yellow outer feathers. The long sharp bill is black at the base and orange at the tip. In the male the base of the bill is edged with orange and there is an orange wattle on each side of the chin. The bill extends over the forehead, giving the oropendola a streamlined appearance. There is a patch of bare skin, white tinged with blue, on each cheek.

## Bubbling songster

Oropendolas live in the Central American forests where they can be seen flying in large straggling flocks searching for food in the tops of the trees or in clearings and along the banks of rivers and pools. Their flight is like that of crows, with a steady, measured beat. The males sing throughout the year, bowing from a perch with the bill below the level of the feet. The song is made up of a large number of very different phrases, as is usual with the songs of icterids. From a distance it is pleasant to hear, but from nearby rasping sounds like rusty machinery can be heard among the continual liquid gurgling and chattering notes. Males also make a characteristic noise as they fly, caused by vibrations of the stiff parts of their flight feathers.

## Sucking nectar

Oropendolas are mainly fruit-eaters but they also drink nectar. They forage among the forest canopy for soft fruit but often come into plantations to eat ripe bananas or to hang upside down and poke their long bills into the banana flowers so as to drink the nectar.

## Hanging nests

Some of the North American icterids are called hangnests after their sacklike nests that are suspended from twigs. The oropendolas and caciques probably most deserve the name as groups of their nests hanging like pendants from the outer branches of trees are a remarkable sight. The nest of the Montezuma oropendola consists of long purses of neatly woven fibres, sometimes up to 6 ft long, that hang from slender branches and twigs or from forks. The entrance is at the top of the purse, and in its position in the outer

△ Colonial life: hanging nests of crested oropendolas, yellow rumped caciques and a bee's nest!
▽ Yellow-rumped caciques **Cacicus cela** (male on the left) are related to the oropendola.

△ *Displaying beside his hanging nest, a male crested oropendola* **Psarocolius decumanus.** *Oropendolas and caciques build their nests so that they hang like pendants from the branches of trees, as illustrated on the opposite page. Because of this habit these birds are often called hangnests.*

reaches of the canopy the nest is very well protected from enemies. Oropendolas are, however, parasitised by cowbirds (p 542).

Alexander Skutch has described the nest-building in considerable detail. The work is done by the females while the males perch nearby singing and keeping watch. Oropendolas are shy and Skutch found observation difficult because the males gave alarm calls as he was approaching, sending the females fleeing into the foliage. The nest material is plant fibres taken from palm leaves. A female oropendola stands on the midrib of the leaf, nicks the undersurface of the midrib with her bill, then tears off a strip of fibres about 2 ft long. The first step in nest-building is to make a foundation of fibres around the chosen twig then to construct a ring of fibres attached to this. The ring forms the entrance of the nest and the oropendola weaves the main body of the nest from this as if knitting a sock. She invariably works from inside the growing nest, always entering and leaving by the proper entrance rather than by the open, unfinished end of the 'sock'. The nest increases in diameter with length, and ends as a round inverted dome lined with leaves. Oropendolas live in colonies with the nests so tightly packed that they may be

woven together and sometimes a twig or branch snaps under the combined weight of nests, broods and sitting parents. A disadvantage of such close nesting is that oropendolas are likely to have pieces of their nests stolen by neighbours while they are away searching for more material, but Skutch found that it is sometimes an advantage for two nests to be woven together. It often happens that a nest is not securely anchored and attachment to another nest may prevent it from falling.

Females outnumber males by about 6 to 1 in each colony. Mating takes place some distance from the nests with the males taking no part in rearing the young, but they are present for the rest of the season, singing and keeping a watch for enemies. Each female lays two white eggs which are incubated for about a fortnight. The chicks spend about a month in the nest being fed on fruit by the female.

## Diversity of birds

The icterids are diverse not only in general appearance but in their feeding and breeding habits and are probably a better example of adaptive radiation than Darwin's finches and the Hawaiian honeycreepers. It is not

easy to realise that the colonial oropendolas with their long purselike nests belong to the same family as cowbirds. Bobolinks and meadowlarks build simple nests of grass stems near the ground. Their social life is quite 'conventional' although two or more females may sometimes be found with one male and the male does little to help in raising the brood. The male melodious blackbird, on the other hand, helps with nest-building.

In general, there is a link between an icterid's diet and its breeding habits. The insect-eaters, such as the melodious blackbird and the cacique, are monogamous and nest solitarily, while the fruit-eaters such as the oropendolas are polygamous and colonial. There are, however, many variations within this framework, such as the promiscuous cowbirds which do not make nests at all.

| class | **Aves** |
|---|---|
| order | **Passeriformes** |
| family | **Icteridae** |
| genus & species | ***Gymnostinops montezuma*** *Montezuma oropendola, others* |

# Oryx

Oryx are among the most beautiful of antelopes, white or fawn in colour, with long back-pointing slender, ridged horns. Their closest relatives are the sable and roan antelopes and the addax. They differ from the former in that the horns sweep back in line with the face instead of rising vertically above the eyes, and from the latter in having smaller hoofs and not having spiral horns.

There are three species all living in the desert areas of Africa and southwest Asia. The very strikingly coloured gemsbok is 4 ft high, and is fawn coloured with a black nose patch and eye stripe uniting to form a 'bridle' round the muzzle. There is a black throat fringe, a black stripe down the back and along the flanks, extending onto the fore- and hindlegs, and white shanks and belly. It has a curiously discontinuous distribution as shown in the map. The northern race, from Somalia, is known as the beisa. Its nose patch does not unite with the lateral face stripes and the only black on the legs is a black patch on the forelegs at the knees, and a black line down the front of them.

Further south is the tufted oryx, which is redder. The face marks are sometimes united, and there are long tufts to the ears.

The second species is the rare Arabian oryx; small and white, it stands 3 ft 6 in. high, and has dark brown or black face marks with a line down the throat, and dark limbs.

The third and most distinctive species is the scimitar oryx found in the Sahara. It has distinctly back-curved horns and is white with reddish head markings and a red neck. The red colour may or may not extend back over the body.

## Dangerous horns

These wary and extraordinarily keen sighted animals wander in herds over large distances. When they are alarmed, the whole herd makes off at a gallop. It has been noticed that the Arabian oryx gallops rather slowly and clumsily compared with the gemsbok. The Arabian oryx also runs straight, whereas the gemsbok twists and turns in its attempts to evade the enemy. When brought to bay, however, the oryx turns on its pursuer, jabbing and butting with its horns; there are cases of lorries, used in capturing oryx, and hunting lions, having been speared by oryx horns. During the rutting season the males fight fiercely but are protected from injury by the

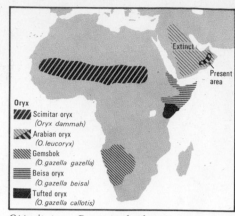

**Oryx**

Scimitar oryx
(*Oryx dammah*)

Arabian oryx
(*O. leucoryx*)

Gemsbok
(*O. gazella gazella*)

Beisa oryx
(*O. gazella beisa*)

Tufted oryx
(*O. gazella callotis*)

*Opposite page: Desert combat between two male beisas (above and centre). Bulls fight one another during the rutting season. These fights can be quite fierce and injuries do occur although the antelopes get some protection from the thickened skin on their shoulders. When injured or brought to bay they attack with their heads lowered so that their sharp horns are pointing well forward. Herd of gemsbok (below). Oryx usually range in small herds of about a dozen although as many as 60 have been seen together. The gemsbok has the longest horns of all the oryx. ▽ The sweeping, graceful arc of the rapier-like horns of the scimitar oryx. Oryx are much hunted as their horns make choice trophies.*

Klaus Paysan

Klaus Paysan

Peter Johnson

thickened skin on their shoulders. Nevertheless slight injuries do occur occasionally.

The herds are small, from half a dozen to a dozen or more. They are composed mainly of females and young, most males living a solitary existence. In the rainy season, the small herds unite into larger groups of as many as two dozen, sometimes up to 60. These herds contain many pregnant females. The herds feed mainly at night or in the early morning, on grass, herbs, fruit and roots.

## Ceremonious courtship

The inherent aggressiveness of the oryx finds unexpected expression in their courtship ceremony. The male and female spar, head to head with horns crossed, pushing with their heads, and moving from side to side, pushing each other round in circles. Then the male rubs the female's hindquarters with his cheek and lays his head on her back. Raising his foreleg horizontally, he strokes the outside of her hindleg, or between her hindlegs—the well known 'Laufschlag' of gazelles, ibex and many other bovids including the oribi. While this goes on, the male's head and body are stretched upwards, and the female lowers her head. These two ceremonies—the sparring and the Laufschlag—alternate several times. This sparring differs from that between two males in that the partners are much closer together, too close to do each other any harm, and the heads are lowered instead of raised. The female may now want to mate, and if so, she will attempt to 'defeat' the male. The couple may whirl round over 20 times. Then the female runs away and the male eagerly pursues her. If the female is willing to mate, the pair circle round 4 or 5 times. The male chases the female, mounts her, clasping her loins with his forelegs and holding his head and neck high, while the female's head is lowered. As in all artiodactyls (the even-toed hoofed mammals) copulation itself takes only a second or two.

The gestation period is 260–300 days. Calves are born in the rainy season, when there is plenty for them and the mothers to eat. In Arabia this is from May to September, but in the Kalahari, where the true gemsbok is found, it is from September to January.

## Keeping cool

The oryx which lives in desert country, must go without water for long stretches. It migrates during the dry season into more fertile areas, the scimitar oryx, for example, migrating out of the Sahara, as far south as 15°N but conditions there are still unbelievably hot and arid. Exactly how they manage to survive in such conditions was not known until CR Taylor published the results of his experiments early in 1969.

When the air temperature is above an animal's temperature, then the animal heats up, and to avoid overheating it loses this extra heat, by sweating or panting. The oryx lives in an environment which is at once hot and dry; it needs to lose heat but if it sweats it will lose valuable water which cannot be replaced.

Taylor found that the oryx can tolerate a considerable rise in body temperature.

△ *An icy stare from a beisa. The only black on the legs of this oryx are patches on its knees.*

△ *On the run: the Arabian oryx is a small, white species that is nearly extinct in the wild.*

▽ *Thanks to the work of Operation Oryx the rare Arabian oryx now breeds successfully in zoos.*

Its normal body temperature is 35°C/96°F. When the air temperature was experimentally raised to 40°C/104°F, the oryx's own body temperature rose 6° to 42°C before evaporation of sweat began to increase and prevent further rise in temperature. With the body temperature above that of the surrounding air, heat was also being lost by conduction and radiation. This was, however, extreme. Usually, when the air was heated to 40°C/104°F, providing the oryx had access to water, its temperature increased only 3—4 Centigrade degrees before sweating accelerated.

When deprived of water, however, oryx do not waste the supply in the body but let their temperature rise, so not only do they not absorb heat, they actually lose it. Inevitably this throws a strain on the body and so if water is available then they use it for evaporation.

The oryx's brain, the part most sensitive to overheating, remains cool while the body temperature goes up. This is because the artery in the neck which carries blood to the brain, the carotid artery, branches into a network of vessels which are close enough to veins bringing cooler blood from the nose to lose heat to them. So, as heat is passed from artery to vein the blood is cooled down before it passes through the delicate brain.

Finally the oryx feeds at night when the relative humidity of the desert air is increased by the drop in temperature. The food plants which are dry and crumbly by day, containing as little as 1% water, absorb moisture at night and within 10 hours, contain 42% water!

# Operation oryx

The rare Arabian oryx was once found throughout Arabia into Syria and Iraq but it is now nearly extinct in the wild although there are a small number in Oman and South Arabia. A few years ago intensive hunting killed large numbers and it was feared there might soon be none left in the wild. On capturing some, it was decided to send them to Phoenix Maytag Zoo, Arizona, where there was a similar desert environment to the Arabian one. The Fauna Preservation Society mounted 'Operation Oryx' in April—May, 1962 and succeeded in capturing two males and one female. These were flown to Phoenix, where they were joined by a female from London Zoo, and one donated by the Sultan of Kuwait. They have bred successfully and there are now 18 in all.

| class | **Mammalia** |
|---|---|
| order | **Artiodactyla** |
| family | **Bovidae** |
| genus & species | ***Oryx dammah*** scimitar oryx |
| | ***O. gazella beisa*** beisa |
| | ***O. gazella callotis*** tufted oryx |
| | ***O. gazella gazella*** gemsbok |
| | ***O. leucoryx*** Arabian oryx |

# Osprey

*This remarkable bird of prey which lives almost exclusively on fish, is a highly effective killer, with 90% of its dives being successful. The osprey, known as the fish-hawk in North America, is the size of a small eagle, and in flight, its long, narrow wings span about 5 ft. Its large toes have long, curved claws and the undersides of the toes are covered with spiny scales that help to hold the fish. The head and short crest are whitish with a black band running through the eye to join the dark plumage of the back. The underparts are white except for a dark band across the breast. The plumage of the sexes is similar but the females are larger. The osprey is almost cosmopolitan. It breeds in North America, northern Asia and much of China and northern and eastern Europe, as well as in scattered places such as southern Spain and the coasts of the Red Sea. In the southern hemisphere it breeds regularly only in Australia and adjacent islands to the north, but will often migrate to South America and South Africa.*

## Spectacular diving

When it hunts, this spectacular fisher circles around over the water on its long wings at a height of 50–100 ft until it spots a fish. It hovers for a moment, then plunges, hitting the water with a great splash; then it surfaces triumphantly to bear its catch back to a perch. The osprey appears to strike the water head-first, but just before the final impact, it throws its feet forwards and enters the water talons first, grabbing the fish with both feet, one in front of the other. Sometimes its dive is so violent that it disappears right under the surface, but at other times it descends gently from the air to pick up its prey from the surface.

The fish that are caught are usually those, such as pike, that bask near the surface, but bream, carp, perch, roach and trout are also frequently caught, depending on the locality. One osprey fishing at sea was found to eat mainly needlefish. On rare occasions ospreys have been found to eat mice, beetles, wounded birds and even chickens, but these items are probably taken when the ospreys are very hungry.

There is a remarkable record of an osprey that met its death from being too good a fisherman: a carp netted in a lake in Germany had the skeleton of an osprey firmly attached to its back. Presumably the carp, which weighed nearly 10 lb, pulled the osprey underwater and drowned it. The talons were so deeply embedded that the corpse could not be freed, so it decomposed while trailing behind the carp. This may be a relatively common death for birds that catch fish in their talons, in the same way as a number of other fish-eaters appear to be choked to death by swallowing bullheads. At the beginning of this century the body of a white-tailed eagle was washed ashore in Shetland with its claws embedded in a large halibut.

## Fish or die

Ospreys spend most of their time circling over water or perched on rocks or trees where there is a good view over the water. They are usually found on the coast but they also haunt lakes and rivers. In Australia they live on the coral islets of the Great Barrier Reef. After the breeding season, ospreys living in more northerly parts migrate to warmer regions, usually following rivers or coastlines but occasionally flying cross-country. In their winter range they may have territories which they defend against other ospreys.

Where they are common, ospreys nest in colonies, with the nests sometimes as little as 60 yd apart. The nest is built mainly of seaweeds, heather, moss, sticks and dead branches, sometimes snapped off trees while in flight. The nest is usually made in a tree or among rocks but may be built on the ground. Ospreys have been persuaded to build their nests on artificial platforms such as cartwheels set on stakes and sometimes they become a nuisance by building on telephone poles or pylons.

△ *A flock of starlings mobs an osprey.*

*Pamela Harrison*

The usual clutch of 3 white eggs with brown markings, is laid in late April or May in Europe and North America. The female does most of the incubation, which lasts about 5 weeks, and during the first 30 days of the chicks' lives she stays on the nest, brooding or shading them. During this period all her food is brought to her by the male. At first the chicks are fed with small lumps of semi-digested fish but later they are given raw strips and when 6 weeks old they are left to tear up fish for themselves. They make their first flights at 7–8 weeks and they either learn to catch their own fish, or perish. Many die in their first year.

## Distraction display

The eggs and chicks fall prey to nest robbers, especially when the parents leave the nest through being disturbed. Crows and raccoons are known to steal eggs and eagles and gulls may do so. The parents often try to lure potential predators away from their nest with a distraction display. They utter loud calls and stagger about in the air with their feet dangling, making themselves conspicuous and taking attention away from the nest.

## Loch Garten ospreys

Like so many birds of prey, ospreys are becoming scarce in many places. In North America DDT picked up from the fish is apparently making the ospreys sterile. They were once fairly abundant in the British Isles, but were almost exterminated by the increase in the numbers of shooting and fishing estates heavily patrolled by gamekeepers; they were finally wiped out by egg-collectors. Then, in 1954, a pair was reported to have bred successfully at Speyside in Scotland. In the following years they were unsuccessful because of disturbance or egg-collecting. Then in 1958 the Royal Society for the Protection of Birds made arrangements to keep a continuous watch on the nest that was built near Loch Garten, but under the cover of darkness the nest was robbed again. Defences were improved and the ospreys bred successfully, except for two years (1963 and 1966) when gales destroyed the nest and in 11 years (1959/1969) 20 young were raised. In 1963 a second pair nested but the eggs did not hatch.

One of the most interesting and surprising features of the nesting at Loch Garten is that anyone can go there and watch the ospreys at the nest. An observation post has been set up nearby and the public, 39 500 in one 16-week season in 1969 viewed the nest through high-power binoculars. This means that the ospreys are not just a hidden treasure. It is, however, unlikely that ospreys will ever breed in their old numbers, simply because of the huge increase in the numbers of people who visit the wild parts of Scotland.

| class | **Aves** |
|---|---|
| order | **Falconiformes** |
| family | **Pandionidae** |
| genus & species | ***Pandion haliaetus*** |

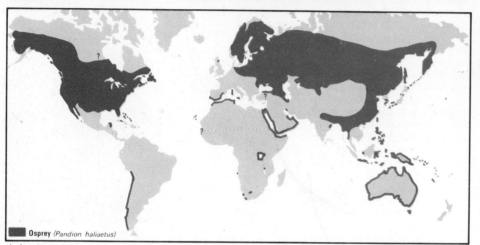

**Osprey** *(Pandion haliaetus)*

△△ *About 60% of young ospreys die in their first year, but this youngster looks very much alive.*

▽ *A fastidious young osprey 'cleans the nest'! The chicks stay on the nest for about 8 weeks.*

△△ *Another successful dive for the osprey.*

△ *An expert fisherman returns with his catch.*

# Ostrich

*The ostrich is the largest living bird and one of the most familiar because of its bizarre appearance. A large male may stand 8 ft high of which nearly half is neck. The plumage of the male is black except for the white plumes on the wings and tail. It is these plumes that first led to the numbers of ostriches being greatly reduced in many places and later to ostriches being raised on farms. The plumage of the females is brown with pale edging to the feathers. The head, most of the neck and the legs are almost naked, but the eyelids have long, black eyelashes. There are two strong toes on each foot, the longest being armed with a large claw.*

*A few million years ago, in the Pliocene era, there were nine species of ostriches, but only one survives today. About 200 years ago five subspecies of this species ranged over much of Africa, Syria and Arabia, in desert and bush regions. They are now extinct or very rare over most of this area. The Asian subspecies was last recorded in 1941. Ostriches are still plentiful in East Africa, and they live wild in a few places in south Australia where they were introduced.*

### Stranger than fiction

Ostriches are extremely wary, their long necks enabling them to detect disturbances from quite a distance. As a result it is very difficult to study ostriches in the wild and until recently our knowledge has been based mainly on observations on domesticated ostriches. Incomplete observations in the wild have led to many mistaken ideas about the habits of these birds which have now become legendary. A husband and wife team of zoologists, the Sauers, studied ostriches in South West Africa by the ingenious method of disguising their hide as a termite mound. Ostriches and several other animals treated this hide with complete indifference with the result that the Sauers were afforded a grandstand view of ostrich social life, and they found that in some respects this is almost as strange as the legends.

Ostriches often live in very dry areas and they move about in search of food, often in quite large groups. During wet spells the herds break up into family groups, consisting of a pair with chicks and immatures. The herd is led by a cock or hen that chooses grazing grounds and makes decisions as to when to move. If the herd leaves familiar territory or comes to a water hole where no other animals are drinking, the dominant ostriches push the immature birds forward to spring any ambushes.

### Avian dustbin

Ostriches feed mainly on plants including fruits, seeds and leaves. In deserts they get their water from succulent plants. They also eat small animals and are even said to eat lizards and tortoises. Their reputation for eating almost anything including lumps of metal and tins of paint is widespread and perhaps exaggerated but ostriches swallow considerable amounts of sand to aid digestion and it is said that it is possible to trace the movements of an ostrich by examining the kinds of sand and gravel in its stomach.

### Unstable society

Until recently there was considerable doubt as to whether ostriches were polygamous or monogamous. Proponents of monogamy pointed out that there was never more than one male or one female seen at a nest or leading a group of chicks. It is now known that ostriches may be monogamous but more usually they are polygamous. The Sauers found that the social organisation of ostriches is very flexible and that a male accompanying a female with chicks need not be the father of the chicks.

Breeding takes place at any time of the year, depending on the time of the rainy season. At first the males develop a red pigment on their heads and feet and they display to each other, chasing around in groups with wings held out to show off the white plumes. Later they establish territories away from the communal feeding grounds, and here they are joined by the females. A male ostrich usually has three hens in his harem but it is not unknown for him to have up to five.

The courtship ceremony is elaborate. The male separates one female from the group and the pair feed together, synchronising the movements of head and neck. The male then sits down and opens his wings to show the white plumes. At the same time he rocks from side to side and twists his neck in a corkscrew. The female walks around him and eventually drops into the mating position.

Each female lays 6–8 eggs which are about 6 in. long and weigh up to $2\frac{1}{2}$ lb. The members of a harem all lay in one nest, which consists of a depression in the ground that may be about 3 yd across. It may take nearly 3 weeks for all the eggs to be laid, after which the dominant hen drives the others away and the nest is guarded by the single hen and the cock. Incubation consists of keeping the eggs cool by shading them rather than keeping them warm. Towards the end of the 6-week incubation period some eggs are rolled into pits on the edge of the nest. These eggs are those that are most advanced and this is probably a mechanism to synchronise the hatching of the eggs as much as possible.

The chicks can run almost as soon as they hatch and after a month can attain a speed of 35 mph. When they leave their parents they form large bands, breeding when 4–5 years old.

### Running to safety

Adult ostriches have little to fear from predators. They are very wary and can run at 40 mph, but the eggs and young ostriches may fall prey to jackals and other predators. The adults lead their chicks away from enemies and perform distraction displays while the chicks scatter and crouch.

▷ *A bizarre creature with a long naked neck: the ostrich is the largest living bird.*

J & M Fievel : Jacana

△△ *A female ostrich keeps her eggs under her protective wing to shade them from the heat.*

△ *A flurry of feathers. A female ostrich displays aggressively in defence of her nest.*

◁ *Fight between a couple of ruffled hens.*

▽ *A female ostrich on her knees, while a male looks on disdainfully from behind.*

Beating their wings and calling loudly the ostriches run to and fro presenting a broadside to the enemy and occasionally dropping to the ground and setting up a cloud of dust with the wings. Sometimes the male continues the display while the female leads the chicks away.

## Burying their heads

One of the popular notions about ostriches is that they bury their heads in the sand when danger threatens. The action is used to describe the behaviour of a person who thinks that a problem can be solved by ignoring it, and has been the subject of many jokes and cartoons. This idea is very old, for the Roman writer Pliny says '. . . the veriest fools they be of all others, for as high as the rest of their body is, yet if they thrust their head and neck once into any shrub

◁ *Too many eggs? At the end of the incubation period the most advanced eggs are rolled into a pit beside the nest to synchronize hatching.*
▽ *Arrival date. Ostrich chicks hatching.*

or bush, and get it hidden, they think then they are safe enough, and that no man seeth them.'

Like so many legends there is a basis of truth in the ostrich burying its head and the story is probably due to the difficulty in observing ostriches. When an ostrich is sitting on the nest, its reaction to disturbance is to lower its head until the neck is held horizontally a few inches above the ground. The ostrich is then very inconspicuous and the small head may well be hidden behind a small plant or hummock.

| class | **Aves** |
|-------|----------|
| order | **Struthioniformes** |
| family | **Struthionidae** |
| genus & species | **Struthio camelus** |

◁ *A handsome male ostrich gives chase to two females busy displaying.*
▽ *Ostriches on the march. Flocks of them move about in the dry season, looking for food.*

# Otter

The various species of otter are all much alike in appearance and habits. They are long-bodied, short-legged mammals, with a stout tail thickened at the root and tapering towards the tip. There is a pair of scent-glands under the tail. The head is flattened with a broad muzzle and numerous bristling whiskers. The ears are small and almost hidden in the fur. The sleek, dark brown fur consists of a close fawn underfur which is waterproof and an outer layer of long stiff guard hairs, which are grey at their bases and brown at their tips. The throat is whitish and the under-parts pale brown. Each foot has five toes, bearing claws in most species, the forefeet are small, the hindfeet large and webbed.

The common or European otter ranges across Europe and parts of Asia, to Japan and the Kurile Islands. It is 4 ft long, including the tail, but may reach $5\frac{1}{2}$ ft, and weighs up to 25 lb. The bitch is smaller than the dog otter. The Canadian otter, of Canada and the United States, is very similar to the European but has an average larger size. It is sometimes spoken of as the river otter, to distinguish it from the sea otter, a markedly different animal. The small-clawed otter, of India and southeast Asia, is much smaller than the European species but the clawless otter of western and southern Africa is larger and is a marsh dweller, feeding on frogs and molluscs. The giant Brazilian otter is the largest of all the otters. It reaches $6\frac{1}{2}$ ft in length, and has a tail that is flattened from side to side.

## Solitary and elusive

Except during the mating season otters are solitary, extremely elusive and secretive, and always alert for any sign of disturbance. They will submerge in a flash, leaving few

▽ Prenuptial affectionate play. Usually solitary, otters are sociable in the mating season.

Albert Visage: Jacana

△ *A backflip from a European otter. These two photos have caught an otter leaping playfully in and out of the water for the pure joy of living.*

▽ *A perfect dive. An otter enters the water gracefully and easily, making hardly a splash.*

ripples or, when on land, they will disappear among vegetation. Their ability to merge into their background on land is helped by the 'boneless' contortions of the body and the changing shades of colour in the coat which is aided by the movements and changes in the guard hairs. For example, the coat can readily pass from looking sleek and smooth to looking, when damp, spiny and almost porcupine-like.

Otters do not hibernate. They will fish under ice with periodic visits to a breathing hole. It has been said that otters will use a trick known in aquatic insects; that is, to come up under ice and breathe out, allowing the 'bubble' to take in oxygen from the air trapped in the ice and lose carbon dioxide to the ice and water, then inhale the re-vitalised 'bubble'. This has not yet been proved, however.

## Master-swimmers

At the surface an otter swims characteristically showing three humps each separated by 5—8 in. of water. The humps are the head, the humped back and the end of the tail curved above the water line. When drifting with the current only the head may be in view. Occasionally an otter may swim with the forelegs held against the flanks, the hindlegs moving so rapidly as to be a blur. When this is done at the surface there is a small area of foam around the hindquarters, with a wake rising in a series of hump-like waves. It will also use this method when submerged, although more commonly it swims with all four legs drawn into the body which, with the tail, is wriggled sinuously, as in an eel. Leaping from the water and plunging in again, in the manner of a dolphin, is another way in which an otter can gain speed in pursuit of a large fish. Underwater it will often progress in a similar, but smoother undulating manner.

An otter shows its skill better in its ability to manoeuvre. It will roll at the surface, or when submerged, pivoting on its long axis, using flicks of the tail to give momentum. It can turn at speed in half its own length, using tail and hindquarters as a rudder, or it may swim round and round in tight circles, creating a vortex that brings mud up from the bottom. This last tactic is used to drag small fishes up that have taken refuge under an overhanging bank.

When an otter surfaces it stretches its neck and turns its flattened, almost reptilian head from side-to-side reconnoitring before swimming at the surface or coming out on land.

Otters are nomads, fishing a river or lake then moving on to take their next meal elsewhere. They are said at times to cover up to 16 miles overland in a night. Certainly the European and Canadian otters are met at times far from the nearest water. Overland they move by humping the back. A favourite trick is to take a couple of bounds then slide on the belly for 4—5 ft. On a steep slope the glide may take them 40—50 ft. On a muddy or snow-covered slope the slide becomes tobogganing, otters often retracing their steps to slide repeatedly down the slope in a form of play.

Otters live in rivers and lakes, especially small rivers running to the sea or to large

△ *African clawless otter **Aonyx capensis**. There is only a small connecting web at the base of the toes, unlike the European otter (right).*

lakes. They particularly like those free of weed and undisturbed by human beings. In times of scarcity otters will move to the coast and are then spoken of as 'sea-otters', not to be confused with the real sea otters.

### Eels and crayfish favoured

The European otter has a varied diet of fish, small invertebrates, particularly crayfish and freshwater mussels, birds, small mammals, frogs and some vegetable matter. The main fish food seems to be eels and slow-moving fishes but salmon and trout are also eaten.

### Otter families play sea-serpents

Mating takes place in water, at any time of the year, with a peak in spring and early summer. After a gestation of about 61 days 2 or 3 cubs, exceptionally 4 or 5, are born, blind and toothless, with a silky coat of dark hair. There is uncertainty about when the eyes open, the only reliable record being 35 days after birth. The cubs stay in the nest for the first 8 weeks and do not leave their mother until just before she mates again.

Young otters swim naturally, as is shown by cubs hand-reared in isolation. The indications are, however, that the mother must coax them, or push them, into the water for their first swim. In the early days of taking to water a cub will sometimes climb onto the mother's back, but normally the cubs swim behind their mother. On rare occasions two or more family parties will swim one behind the other. When this does happen a line of humps is seen, and as the leading otter periodically raises her head to take a look around the procession resembles the traditional picture of the sea-serpent.

## Otters as lake monsters

It has been said that any schoolboy knows an otter when he sees one. This is so only as long as the otter runs true to form, but otters are quick-change artists and highly deceptive. Sir Herbert Maxwell has recorded how, at the turn of the century, four gentlemen crossing Loch Arkaig in a steam pinnace saw a 'monster' rise from the depths almost under the bows of their boat, create a tremendous flurry of water at the surface, then dive again out of sight. All were puzzled as to its identity, but when the stalker, a Highlander, present with them in the boat, was questioned later, he was in no doubt that the 'monster' was an otter.

The monster of Loch Morar, near Loch Arkaig, is traditionally 'like an overturned boat towing three overturned dinghies', which could serve as a reasonable description of a bitch otter followed by her three cubs. The ogo-pogo of Canada is believed to be founded on otters swimming in line, and at least one lake monster in Kenya was proved to be a line of otters.

When President Theodore Roosevelt was big game hunting in 1911 he was out in a boat on Lake Naivasha, in Kenya, when the three humps of the local monster appeared. Roosevelt fired once, two humps disappeared, the third stayed on the surface. The skin of the otter was sent to the American Museum of Natural History in New York.

| class | **Mammalia** |
|---|---|
| order | **Carnivora** |
| family | **Mustelidae** |
| genera & species | **Amblonyx cinerea** *Indian small-clawed otter* **Aonyx capensis** *clawless otter* **Lutra canadensis** *Canadian otter* **L. lutra** *European otter* **Pteronura brasiliensis** *giant Brazilian otter* *others* |

▽ *Family outing for a group of young otters. Usually there are only two or three cubs in a litter.*

▷*On the brink. A European otter about to dive.*

# Otter shrew

*The largest of the three species of otter shrew, all of which are African, does in fact look like a miniature otter. It is known as the giant otter shrew. Its head and body length can be up to 14 in. with a stout tail up to 12 in. long. The tail tapers to the tip and is flattened from side to side. The smooth, sleek fur is made up of a short, soft, dense underfur with a covering of long coarse guard hairs. It is chocolate-brown to blackish on the back and flanks, and white to yellowish on the underparts including the throat and chin. The short legs have five toes on each foot, without webbing. A peculiarity is that the second and third toes on the hindfeet are joined by skin. The flattened head has a long muzzle, small ears and very tiny, probably useless, eyes. Each nostril has a flap of skin that acts as a valve when the animal is underwater. The end of the snout is swollen, almost duck-billed, and has many long whiskers which act as organs of touch and are next in importance to a sense of smell.*

*The dwarf African otter shrews are less than a foot long, brownish grey above and grey below. The toes are partly webbed and the tail, keeled above and below, is round and covered with short hair. The two dwarf otter shrews look more like the true water shrews and, like them, and in contrast with the giant otter shrew, they swim by paddling with their feet.*

*The giant otter shrew lives in western and central tropical Africa, from sea-level to 6 000 ft. One of the two dwarf species lives in the coastal regions of West Africa, the other, in the Congo.*

## River bank hermit

The giant otter shrew lives in sluggish, muddy lowland streams as well as clear mountain streams. In some places it lives in forest pools in the rainy season and migrates to rivers in the dry season. It is a solitary animal, pairing only to breed. It starts to be active 2—2½ hours after nightfall, and throughout the night until first light it alternates feeding with resting in irregular periods. During the day it shelters in burrows in the banks of streams. The entrance to a burrow is above water level. The tunnel goes for a long way into the bank then forks. One branch leads to a sleeping chamber in which is a nest of dry leaves laid neatly one on top of the other. The other branch leads down and opens farther along the bank underwater. Although the shrew moves awkwardly on land it can run at a fair speed. It swims rapidly and easily with a sculling action of the tail and serpentine movements of the body, legs pressed against the sides. On leaving the water the first thing it does is to scratch its belly vigorously with the 2nd and 3rd toes on the hindfoot, then lick its feet and its genital organs. This is the limit of its grooming.

## Mainly crabs to eat

As with many aquatic animals, otter shrews probe among mud or under stones for crabs, the long whiskers probably acting as organs of touch. Food is brought onto land to be eaten. Some reports say it eats only crabs, others that it also eats fish and frogs. Dubost, who has made an extensive study of otter shrews, examined the stomachs of trapped animals and found fish remains predominated. After this came crabs and crayfish and insects and their larvae, with no sign of frogs having been eaten. One peculiarity is that when an otter shrew is feeding it allows nothing to disturb it. Even when put in a cage, after being captured, if food is put in it immediately gets down to feeding. When eating a crab the otter shrew turns it on its back and tears out the flesh from the softer underside. One giant otter shrew in captivity ate up to 20 small crabs in one night. Dwarf otter shrews sometimes get into fish traps and kill all the fish before they themselves drown, being unable to escape.

## Romance of otter shrews

Although otter shrews are trapped in hundreds by African hunters, and although all the evidence is that they are very common, little is known of their habits. The only family party seen was a female and her two babies. It seems possible that there are one or two at a birth and that there are two breeding seasons a year. AH Booth, in his *Small Mammals of West Africa*, says the otter shrew is hard to trap and owing to its nocturnal habits it is difficult to find out about its way of life. 'Moreover it is one of those Cameroons mammals which have suffered from romantic, rather than strictly accurate naturalists. As a result, even the little that we do know is clouded by uncertainty.' One of the romantic naturalists Booth had in mind was probably Paul du Chaillu, the French-American explorer, who discovered the giant otter shrew in 1861. Du Chaillu had written a book describing his adventures in West Africa, including the most hair-raising stories about the ferocity of gorillas. He was severely criticized by scientists at the time and although he gave sober accounts of the hammerheaded bat and other animals, which he also discovered, they were viewed with scepticism. One of these was his 'swift river-weasel', a name which, when translated to scientific terms, gives *Potamogale velox*. The fact that it is neither a weasel nor an otter but a shrew need not diminish the credit due to du Chaillu for discovering it even if his account of it was a little highly coloured.

| class | **Mammalia** |
|---|---|
| order | **Insectivora** |
| family | **Potamogalidae** |
| genera & species | *Potamogale velox* <br> giant otter shrew <br> ***Micropotamogale lamottei*** <br> dwarf otter shrew <br> ***M. ruwenzorii*** <br> dwarf otter shrew |

*Giant otter shrew. It has a cylindrical body and a thick, powerful tail which seems to be its only means of propulsion in the water.*